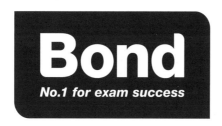
Bond
No.1 for exam success

English
10 Minute Tests

10–11⁺ years

OXFORD
UNIVERSITY PRESS

Rewrite these sentences changing them from plural to singular.

1 The leaves fell from the trees.

_____

2 The children played with two skipping ropes and some footballs.

_____

3 While playing, the kittens knocked the bags to the floor.

_____

4 The swings broke and injured many children.

_____

Change each of the nouns in **bold** to the *infinitive* of the verb.

5 Amil needed more practice with his **division**. to _____

6 A **statement** was read out by the lawyer. to _____

7 The **infection** had spread to Ella's ears. to _____

8 The burglar was caught by the **detective**. to _____

Write an *antonym* for each of these words by adding a prefix.

9 happy _____ **12** correct _____

10 frost _____ **13** clean _____

11 grateful _____ **14** advantage _____

Complete the following proverbs.

15   Too many cooks _____ .

16   The grass is always greener _____ .

17   _____ the mice will play.

18   _____ has a silver lining.

19   The early bird _____ .

Write 'there', 'their' or 'they're' in the gap.

20   The children collected _____ bags before going home.

21–22   James and Sarah love _____ dog and _____ always taking
him on long walks.

23   _____ is never enough money collected to help look after the homeless.

Complete these word sums. Watch out for the spelling changes!

24   busy + ly =   _____

25   argue + ment =   _____

26   laugh + ing =   _____

27   notice + able =   _____

28   complete + ly =   _____

29   imagine + ary =   _____

30   meaning + less =   _____

Total

TEST 2: **Spelling**

Test time: 0 — 5 — 10 minutes

Write each of these words correctly.

1 unecessary _____

2 desparate _____

3 recomend _____

4 apreciate _____

5 haras _____

6 detemined _____

7 bargin _____

8 enviroment _____

9 interupt _____

10 curiocity _____

Add a prefix to each of these to make a new word.

11 behave _____

12 charge _____

13 cycle _____

14 mobile _____

15 ready _____

16 fortune _____

Write four words, two ending in *cial* and two ending in *tial*.

17–18 _____   _____

19–20 _____   _____

4

Write the plural forms of these words.

21 church   _____

22 waltz   _____

23 bush   _____

24 pencil   _____

25 wife   _____

Add ie or ei to each of these to make a word.

26 br ___ ___ f   **30** f ___ ___ nt

27 sl ___ ___ gh   **31** s ___ ___ ge

28 ___ ___ ghty   **32** r ___ ___ gn

29 f ___ ___ rce   **33** c ___ ___ ling

Each of these words has a missing silent letter. Rewrite each word correctly.

34 nockout   _____

35 colum   _____

36 miniture   _____

37 salm   _____

38 nat   _____

39 climer   _____

40 nome   _____

Total [   ]

Nat and the Great Bath Climb   *by Penelope Lively*

Wood-lice colonies are governed by Chief Wood-lice, who are stern and ancient creatures with whiskers of immense length. Young wood-lice are kept under the most strict control by their elders; indeed they are quite literally trampled on until large enough to hold their own. Wood-lice are not creatures who go in much for expressing themselves or being original or striking out; one wood-louse acts and thinks much like another and this is the way the old wood-lice want to keep it.

From time to time the Chief Wood-louse would call the whole colony together for a meeting. The object of this meeting was for the Chief Wood-louse to lecture the newest generation of young wood-lice, who were allowed to attend as soon as their whiskers were three millimetres long, which meant they were grown-up.

The hero of this story, who was called Nat, came to his first such meeting when he was three weeks old – which in human terms is about eighteen years. The young wood-lice sat in a row at the front, feeling important but nervous, while their parents and aunts and uncles crowded behind them and the Chief Wood-louse took up a position in front.

The Chief Wood-louse looked sternly down at the **assembled** crowd and began to speak. "We are gathered together today," he said, "to remind ourselves of the purpose of life." He glared at the young wood-lice. "And what is the purpose of life?" The young wood-lice, who knew they were not supposed to answer, gazed at him respectfully.

"The purpose of life is to climb up the side of the bath. That is what we are here for. That is why we were born. No one has ever succeeded. But the purpose of life is to try. Each and every one of us. Your turn has now come. Your mothers and fathers have tried before you. Some brave spirits have tried several times. All have failed."

There was silence. The young wood-lice gazed at the Chief Wood-louse and felt even more nervous and important. All except Nat, who was the youngest and smallest and had been in trouble most of his life for asking too many questions. Nat was thinking.

"You will make your attempts turn and turn about, starting with the eldest. Each of you will fail, but will have made a glorious attempt, you will then have your names inscribed on the Roll of Honour."

The young wood-lice went quite pink with pride and excitement, all except Nat, who raised one of his fourteen legs. "Please, sir," he said, "why do we have to climb up the side of the bath?"

There was a gasp of horror from the crowd of wood-lice. Nat's mother fainted clean away; his father bent his head in shame.

The Chief Wood-louse stared at Nat. His whiskers twitched in fury. "WHAT DID YOU SAY?"

Nat cleared his throat and repeated, politely and clearly, "Why do we have to climb up the side of the bath?"

The Chief Wood-louse huffed and puffed; his little black eyes bulged; **he creaked with indignation**. "BECAUSE IT'S THERE!" he roared…

Answer these questions about the extract.

1 Who controls young wood-lice?

_____

2 Write a sentence describing what wood-lice elders are like.

_____

_____

3 How long do wood-lice whiskers have to be before wood-lice are considered to be grown-up?

_____

4 How do you think the parents of the young wood-lice felt, waiting for the Chief Wood-louse to begin the meeting?

_____

_____

5 What is the meeting for?

_____

6 Why had Nat been in trouble for most of his life?

_____

7 What does the word **'assembled'** mean? _____

8 What is meant by **'he creaked with indignation'**?

_____

9 Why were all the wood-lice shocked when Nat asked a question?

_____

10 What do you think happened next?

_____

_____

Total [   ]

Add to each of these words to make a compound word.

1   sun   _____

2   hand   _____

3   snow   _____

4   pen   _____

5   light   _____

6   trap   _____

7   foot   _____

8   rain   _____

Change these sentences into *indirect speech*.

9   "If we don't hurry we'll be late," shouted Zoe.

_____

10 Beth enquired, "Is this the way to the toilets?"

_____

11 "Quick, the guard dog is catching us!" screamed Dan.

_____

_____

12 "What time is it?" asked Mrs Sparks.

_____

13 Mum whispered, "Remember, when you wake up in the morning it will be your birthday!"

_____

_____

Write a *homophone* for each of these words.

14 cereal   _____

15 great   _____

16 horse   _____

17 bough   _____

18 beach   _____

19 heard   _____

20 wait   _____

21 piece   _____

22 sent   _____

Punctuate this passage correctly. Remember to start a new line when it is needed.

23–40 Class 6 was having a swimming lesson I'm exhausted exclaimed Eva I wish something more exciting would happen I agree because if I do one more length of this pool I'll scream moaned Lee Suddenly Eva's wish came true as Mrs Davey their teacher slipped on some water at the side of the pool She fell headfirst into the pool

_____

_____

_____

_____

_____

_____

_____

_____

Total ⬜

Write an informal equivalent for each of these words.

1   request   _____

2   displeasure   _____

3   unavoidable   _____

4   discover   _____

5   **enter**   _____

Write six *synonyms* for the word 'said'.

6   _____   9   _____

7   _____   10   _____

8   _____   11   _____

Write a definition for each of the underlined *idioms*.

12   James felt <u>over the moon</u> when he won the trophy.

_____

13   Meena was feeling <u>under the weather</u> having eaten five bags of crisps.

_____

14   Ben <u>had a change of heart</u>; he didn't want to play outside in the rain!

_____

Write a definition for each of these words.

15 ponder _____

16 unmistakable _____

17 cooperate _____

18 occupation _____

19 percentage _____

20 submerge _____

Circle the *diminutives*.

21–25 duckling calf piglet

eaglet bullock fawn

lamb owlet foal

Complete each sentence as a *simile*.

26 Aimee's bed was as warm as _____.

27 Jacob ran as fast as _____.

28 The custard was as thick as _____.

29 Jess felt as cold as _____.

30 Tom's bruise was as big as _____.

Total

Circle the silent letter in each of these words.

1   guilt

2   knuckle

3   rhombus

4   island

5   gnat

6   crescent

7   crumb

8   answer

What are the following: commands, questions or statements?

9   Put your homework on the table   _____

10   What time is our appointment   _____

11   Global warming is a serious problem   _____

12   It's six o'clock   _____

13   Where have I put my recorder   _____

14   Sit quietly   _____

Add the missing apostrophes.

15–16   Ill run and get my coat from Henrys house.

17   Wheres my hat?

18   Isnt it time the cinema doors opened?

Write four words used in English but derived from another language.
Example: croissant

19 _____

20 _____

21 _____

22 _____

What parts of speech are each of these words?

23 after _____

24 scream _____

25 he _____

26 tarantula _____

27 frantically _____

Write three sentences, each using the given phrases.

28 as a consequence

_____

29 on the other hand

_____

30 in contrast to

_____

Total _____

TEST 7: **Grammar**

Write two examples of each of the following.

1–2   common nouns   _____   _____

3–4   abstract nouns   _____   _____

5–6   proper nouns   _____   _____

7–8   collective nouns   _____   _____

Fill each gap with an _adverb_.

9   Matthew looked _____ at the sweets.

10   Hannah copied her story _____.

11   The Gallop family _____ waved goodbye to their cousins.

12   Jacob _____ tidied his messy room.

Write two _adjectives_ to describe each of these nouns.

13–14   _____ , _____ hair

15–16   a _____ , _____ lion

17–18   a _____ , _____ butterfly

Write two sentences that begin with _fronted adverbials_.

19   _____

20   _____

Underline the *preposition* in each sentence.

21   Shall we meet after breakfast?

22   Jessica's cat slept on her bed.

23   Let's see how far we can swim under the water.

24   Carl jumped over the broken gate.

Write three sentences, each with a *comparative adjective* and a *conjunction*.

25–26 _____

_____

_____

27–28 _____

_____

_____

29–30 _____

_____

_____

Total

Test time: 0   5   10 minutes

Read this poem carefully.

The Sands of Dee

"O Mary, go and call the cattle home,
And call the cattle home,
And call the cattle home,
Across the sands of Dee;"
The western wind was wild and dank with foam,
And all alone went she.

The western tide crept up along the sand,
And o'er and o'er the sand,
And round and round the sand,
As far as eye could see.
The rolling mist came down and hid the land:
And never home came she.

"Oh, is it weed, or fish, or floating hair –
A tress of golden hair,
A drowned maiden's hair
Above the nets at sea?
Was never salmon yet that shone so fair
Among the stakes on Dee."

They rowed her in across the rolling foam,
The cruel, crawling foam,
The cruel, hungry foam,
To her grave beside the sea:
But still the boatmen hear her call the cattle home,
Across the sands of Dee.

by Charles Kingsley

Answer these questions about the poem.

1 What was Mary asked to do?

_____

2 When Mary set off, what was the weather like?

_____

3 'The rolling mist came down and hid the land:'
   What image does this line conjure up in your mind?

_____

_____

4 Copy the line in the poem that informs us of Mary's death.

_____

5 Why do you think the sea foam is described as cruel?

_____

_____

6 Where was Mary buried?

_____

7 Which word in the poem means damp or moist? _____

8 What does 'o'er' mean? _____

9 How do you think Mary felt when she was sent out to the sands of Dee?

_____

_____

10 Describe how this poem makes you feel.

_____

_____

_____

TEST 9: **Mixed**

Underline the correct verb form in each sentence.

1   When (is/are) we going to get to Gran's house?

2   (Is/Are) we meeting this afternoon?

3   Todd's parents (was/were) pleased with his progress.

4   It (was/were) raining outside.

5   Which pony (is/are) Jodie's?

Add *tious* or *cious* to complete each word.

6   suspi   _____

7   infec   _____

8   ambi   _____

9   vi   _____

10   nutri   _____

Write each of these words correctly.

11   embarras   _____

12   seperate   _____

13   marvelous   _____

14   vegtable   _____

15   resturant   _____

Write a short conversation between two friends discussing what they might do after school. Be careful to start new lines when they are needed and to punctuate the conversation correctly.

16–25

_____

_____

_____

_____

_____

_____

_____

_____

_____

_____

Write five *synonyms* for the word 'nice'.

26   _____

27   _____

28   _____

29   _____

30   _____

Total

Test time: 0 ——|—|—|—|—|—|—|—|—|—|— 10 minutes

5

| Write these statements as questions. |

1 The water is too deep to swim in.

_____

2 Andy is hiding in the woods.

_____

3 Bola isn't allowed out on his bike.

_____

4 My birthday is in February.

_____

5 It takes Sophie thirty minutes to walk to school.

_____

| Write two sentences. Each sentence needs to have two commas. |

6–7 _____

_____

8–9 _____

_____

20

Rewrite this short passage correctly. Remember to begin a new line when a different person starts to speak.

10–20 Is it Gym Club tonight asked Thomas It always is on Monday replied Poppy Thomas groaned he'd forgotten his PE kit again

_____

_____

_____

Rewrite these sentences without double negatives.

21 We didn't want no homework.

_____

22 Jake hasn't no problem learning his spellings.

_____

23 Dad couldn't find no gap in which to park his car.

_____

Write two sentences that indicate parenthesis using commas, brackets or dashes.

24 _____

25 _____

Total

TEST 11: **Mixed**

Test time: 0   5   10 minutes

Draw lines to link each old word with the modern word.

1	saith	are
2	remaineth	here
3	hither	says
4	abides	remain
5	art	lives

Complete each sentence with a *phrase* or *clause*.

6 Miss James _____

_____ waited for the class to listen.

7 The cat _____

_____ pounced on its prey.

8 Todd's computer _____

_____ frequently broke down.

9 The policeman _____

_____ kept an eye on the man.

10 The sun _____

_____ melted the ice cream in minutes.

22

Write two words, at least one hyphenated, using each of these prefixes.

11–12   bi   _____   _____

13–14   non   _____   _____

15–16   cross   _____   _____

17–18   co   _____   _____

19–20   re   _____   _____

Fill each gap with an *adjective* and noun.

21   Sam screamed and ran from the _____.

22   Jack snuggled closer to the _____.

23   Freda rushed towards the _____.

24   Joseph raced after the _____.

Add 'able' or 'ible' to complete each word.

25   charge_____

26   irresist_____

27   convert_____

28   extend_____

29   regrett_____

30   avoid_____

Total _____

Test time: 0   5   10 minutes

List five *ough* words. Each word must illustrate a different pronunciation of the *ough* letter pattern.

1–5

_____

_____

_____

_____

_____

Write each of these words correctly.

6 imediately   _____

7 relevent   _____

8 secratary   _____

9 temprature   _____

10 excellant   _____

Add ance or ence to each of these to make a word.

11 appear_____   **14** occurr_____

12 eleg_____   **15** sil_____

13 radi_____   **16** experi_____

Add ant or ent to each of these to make a word.

17 pleas_____   **20** abund_____

18 hesit_____   **21** stagn_____

19 magnific_____   **22** transpar_____

TEST 1: Mixed (pages 2–3)

1 **The <u>leaf</u> fell from the <u>tree</u>**. If a word ends in '-f' or '-fe', add 'ves' to form the plural. (There are some exceptions, such as 'cliffs'.) If a word ends in a vowel, add 's'.

2 **The <u>child</u> played with <u>a</u> skipping <u>rope</u> and <u>a football</u>**. Some words change completely as plurals, e.g. child – children, mouse – mice.

3 **While playing, the <u>kitten</u> knocked the <u>bag</u> to the floor**.

4 **The <u>swing</u> broke and injured <u>a child</u>**. Refer to Q2.

5–8 Refer to definition of infinitives in key words on page 47.

5 **to divide**   6 **to state**
7 **to infect**   8 **to detect**

9–14 Refer to definition of antonyms in key words on page 47. A prefix is a group of letters added to the beginning of a root word to make a new word.

9 **unhappy**   10 **defrost**
11 **ungrateful**   12 **incorrect**
13 **unclean**   14 **disadvantage**

15–19 A proverb is a well-known saying.

15 **Too many cooks spoil the broth.**
16 **The grass is always greener on the other side.**
17 **While the cat's away the mice will play.**
18 **Every cloud has a silver lining.**
19 **The early bird catches the worm.**

20–23 A quick way of remembering which word to use is that 'there' is connected to the words 'here' and 'where'. An apostrophe shows where there are missing letters in a contraction so 'they're' is a shortened form of 'they are'. 'Their' means 'belonging to them'.

20 **their** The children collected their bags before going home.

21–22 **their**, **they're** James and Sarah love their dog and they're always taking him on long walks.

23 **There** There is never enough money collected to help look after the homeless.

24 **busily** When adding the suffix '-ly', just add it to the root word unless it ends in a 'y', which should then change to an 'i'; if the root word ends in '-le', change the '-le' to '-ly'.

25 **argument** The suffix '-ment' can usually be added to the root word with no spelling change; however, as in this example, there are some exceptions (in this case, the 'e' has been removed).

26 **laughing** When adding the suffix '-ing', just add it to the root word. There are some exceptions: if the root word ends in '-e', it is sometimes removed (e.g. 'love' becomes 'loving'); if the root word ends in a short vowel and consonant, double the consonant before adding '-ing' (e.g. 'run' becomes 'running')

27 **noticeable** When adding the suffix '-able', just add it to the root word. There are some exceptions; if the root word ends in '-e', it is sometimes removed, e.g. 'love' becomes 'lovable'. However, this word is an exception to this exception!

28 **completely** Refer to Q24.

29 **imaginary** As with many suffixes, '-ary' can usually be added to the root word without any changes, unless the root word ends in an '-e', which is then removed.

30 **meaningless** The suffix '-less' can generally be added to the root word without any change in spelling.

TEST 2: Spelling (pages 4–5)

1 **unnecessary**   2 **desperate**
3 **recommend**   4 **appreciate**
5 **harass**   6 **determined**
7 **bargain**   8 **environment**
9 **interrupt**   10 **curiosity**

11–16 Refer to Test 1 Mixed Q9–14.

11 *misbehave*   12 *recharge*
13 *tricycle*   14 *automobile*
15 *unready*   16 *misfortune*

17–20 In most cases, 'tial' is used if it follows a consonant, and 'cial' is used if it follows a vowel. (There are some exceptions, such as 'spatial'.)

17–18 Possible answers: *special, official*
19–20 Possible answers: *partial, substantial*

21 **churches** If a word ends in '-s', '-sh', '-ch', '-x' or '-z', add 'es' to form the plural.

22 **waltzes** Refer to Q21.

23 **bushes** Refer to Q21.

24 **pencils** For words not ending in '-s', '-sh', '-ch', '-x' or '-z', add 's'.

25 **wives** Refer to Test 1 Mixed Q1.

26–33 Although the general 'i before e except after c' rule can be applied sometimes, there are many exceptions. When the sound is ee, use 'ie' (e.g. belief); when the sound is ay, use 'ei' (e.g. neighbour). As usual, there are also some exceptions to this rule, such as caffeine.

26 **br*ie*f** The ee sound means it is spelt 'ie'.

27 **sl*ei*gh** The ay sound means it is spelt 'ei'.

28 eighty Refer to Q27.
29 fierce Refer to Q26.
30 feint Refer to Q27.
31 siege Refer to Q26.
32 reign Refer to Q27.
33 ceiling 'i before e, except after c.'
34 knockout
35 column
36 miniature
37 psalm
38 gnat
39 climber
40 gnome

TEST 3: Comprehension (pages 6–7)

1 **their elders** (line 5)
2 *Wood-lice elders are strict and set in their ways.* (lines 5 and 10–12)
3 **3 millimetres** (para 2 line 7)
4 *proud that their young were attending the meeting but also probably a little nervous*
5 *to remind themselves of the purpose of life* (para 4 lines 4–5)
6 *asking too many questions* (para 6 lines 5–6)
7 *brought together*
8 *he moved with displeasure*
9 *because nobody ever asked the Chief Wood-louse questions*
10 Child's own answer. This could include other Wood-louse asking questions, or watching each Wood-lice climb the bath, or Nat's parents withdrawing him from the meeting in embarrassment.

TEST 4: Mixed (pages 8–9)

1–8 A compound word is a word formed from two other words. Possible answers include the following:
1 *sunlight*   2 *handbag*
3 *snowball*   4 *penknife*
5 *lighthouse*   6 *trapdoor*
7 *football*   8 *rainfall*
9–13 Refer to definition of indirect speech in key words on page 47.
9 **Zoe shouted that if we didn't hurry we'd be late.** The contractions may be written as two words, e.g. 'did not' instead of 'didn't'.
10 **Beth enquired whether that was the way to the toilets.**
11 **Dan screamed that we had to be quick as the guard dog was catching us.** A different conjunction with a similar meaning may be used instead of 'as', such as 'because'.
12 **Mrs Sparks asked what time it was**.

13 **Mum whispered to remind me that when I woke up in the morning it would be my birthday.** The word order may be slightly different, e.g. 'Mum whispered that I should remember when I woke up…'
14–22 Refer to definition of homophones in key words on page 47.
14 **serial**   15 **grate**
16 **hoarse**   17 **bow**
18 **beech**   19 **herd**
20 **weight**   21 **peace**
22 **scent** or **cent**
23–40 Class 6 was having a swimming lesson.
"I'm exhausted," exclaimed Eva. "I wish something more exciting would happen."
"I agree because if I do one more length of this pool I'll scream!" moaned Lee.
Suddenly, Eva's wish came true as Mrs Davey, their teacher, slipped on some water at the side of the pool. She fell headfirst into the pool!

TEST 5: Vocabulary (pages 10–11)

1 *ask for*
2 *unhappiness*
3 *unable to avoid*
4 *find out*
5 *go in*
6–11 Refer to definition of synonyms in key words on page 47. Possible answers include *cried, exclaimed, laughed, replied, shouted*
12–14 Refer to definition of idioms in key words on page 47.
12 *very pleased*
13 *sick or ill*
14 *changed his mind*
15–20 Any definition that approximates the ones given below is acceptable.
15 *to think carefully about something*
16 *clear, obvious*
17 *to work willingly with others*
18 *a job or something to fill one's time*
19 *something divided into a hundred parts*
20 *to go under water*
21–25 **duckling, piglet, eaglet, bullock, owlet**. Refer to definition of diminutives in key words on page 47.
26–30 Refer to definition of similes in key words on page 47. Possible answers include:
26 *toast*
27 *a cheetah*
28 *cement*
29 *ice*
30 *an apple*

TEST 6: Mixed (pages 12–13)

1	u	2	k	3	h
4	s	5	g	6	c
7	b	8	w		

9–14 Commands begin with an imperative verb and tend to omit the subject of the sentence, e.g. "Eat your dinner." Questions usually begin with a question word and require a response. Statements generally contain a subject, verb and object.

9	**command**	10	**question**
11	**statement**	12	**statement**
13	**question**	14	**command**

15–18 Apostrophes are used for contractions (also known as for omission, when two words are combined and a letter is omitted)' e.g. 'do not' becomes 'don't', with the apostrophe indicating the missing o, and to show possession, e.g. the shoe belonging to Joe = Joe's shoe.

15–16 **I'll run and get my coat from <u>Henry's</u> house.** Contraction of 'I' + 'will' and possession.

17 **<u>Where's</u> my hat?** Contraction of 'Where' + 'is'.

18 **<u>Isn't</u> it time the cinema doors opened?** Contraction of 'Is' + 'not'.

19–22 Possible answers include *pizza*, *origami*, *umbrella*, *siesta*.

23 **preposition or conjunction** e.g. 'I ate tea after 5pm' or 'I ate tea after I cleaned my room'

24 **verb or noun** e.g. 'I scream' or 'I heard a scream'

25 **pronoun**

26 **noun**

27 **adverb**

28–30 Child's own answers.

TEST 7: Grammar (pages 14–15)

1–2 A common noun is a noun referring to a person, place or thing – it is not capitalised. Possible answers include *chair*, *house*.

3–4 Refer to definition of abstract nouns in key words on page 47. Possible answers include *love*, *beauty*.

5–6 A proper noun is a noun referring to the name of something – it is capitalised. Possible answers include *Beth*, *England*.

7–8 Refer to definition of collective nouns in key words on page 47. Possible answers include *crowd*, *gaggle*.

9–12 Refer to definition of adverbs in key words on page 47. Here are some possible answers:

9	*longingly*	10	*neatly*
11	*sadly*	12	*grumpily*

13–18 Refer to definition of adjectives in key words on page 47. Here are some possible answers:

13–14 *long, black*

15–16 *large, snarling*

17–18 *small, fragile*

19–20 Refer to definition of fronted adverbials in key words on page 47. A possible answer could be *Under the stairs*, he found a large hole.

21–24 Refer to definition of prepositions in key words on page 47.

21	**after**	22	**on**
23	**under**	24	**over**

25–30 Refer to definitions of comparative adjectives and conjunctions in key words on page 47. Child's own answers must include one of each per sentence. An example sentence would be *The girl was tall, <u>even though</u> she was <u>younger</u> than the others*.

TEST 8: Comprehension (pages 16–17)

1 **call the cattle home** (lines 1–3)

2 *there was a wild wind* (line 5)

3 Child's own answers. This could include interpretations of personification, such as the weather purposely hiding the land to make it difficult for Mary to return.

4 **A drowned maiden's hair** (line 15)

5 *it was the sea foam in which Mary died*

6 *beside the sea* (line 22)

7 **dank** (line 5)

8 **over**

9 Child's own answer, e.g. *nervous*.

10 Child's own answer.

TEST 9: Mixed (pages 18–19)

1 When **are** we going to get to Gran's house?

2 **Are** we meeting this afternoon?

3 Todd's parents **were** pleased with his progress.

4 It **was** raining outside.

5 Which pony **is** Jodie's?

6–10 The suffix '-tious' is usually used when the root word can also have a '-tion' ending. If the root word ends in '-ce', the suffix '-cious' is usually used (of course, there are exceptions).

6 **suspicious**

7 **infectious** The word 'infec<u>tion</u>' can also be made from the root word.

8 **ambitious** The word 'ambi<u>tion</u>' can also be made from the root word.

9 **vicious** The root word is 'vi<u>ce</u>'.

10 **nutritious** The word 'nutri<u>tion</u>' can also be made from the root word.

11 **embarrass**
12 **separate**
13 **marvellous**
14 **vegetable**
15 **restaurant**
16–25 Child's own answer. Give marks for correct layout and punctuation.
26–30 Refer to definition of synonyms in key words on page 47. Possible answers include: *pleasant, lovely, enjoyable, good, likeable.*

TEST 10: Sentences (pages 20–21)

1 **Is the water too deep to swim in?**
2 **Is Andy hiding in the woods?**
3 **Isn't Bola allowed out on his bike?**
4 **Is my birthday in February?**
5 **Does it take Sophie thirty minutes to walk to school?**
6–9 Commas are used to separate items in a list. There is a comma between each item except for the final two, which are separated by 'and' instead. Commas are also used to separate the main clause in a sentence from the additional added information. Child's own answers.
10–20 "Is it Gym Club tonight?" asked Thomas. "It always is on Monday," replied Poppy. Thomas groaned. He'd forgotten his PE kit again.
21 **We didn't want any homework**.
22 **Jake hasn't a problem learning his spellings**. or **Jake has no problem learning his spellings**.
23 **Dad couldn't find a gap in which to park his car**. or **Dad could find no gap in which to park his car**.
24–25 Refer to definition of parenthesis in key words on page 47. For example: *Jess and her friends (Aman and Janice) caught the bus to town*.

TEST 11: Mixed (pages 22–23)

1 **saith – says**
2 **remaineth – remain**
3 **hither – here**
4 **abides – lives**
5 **art – are**
6–10 Refer to definitions of phrases and clauses in key words on page 47. Child's own answers.
11–20 Refer to Test 1 Mixed Q9–14. Here are some possible answers.
11–12 *bi-monthly, bicycle*
13–14 *non-smoker, nonsense*

15–16 *cross-section, crossroad*
17–18 *co-operate, coexist*
19–20 *re-cover, rewrite*
21–24 Refer to definition of adjectives in key words on page 47. Possible answers include:
21 *haunted house*   23 *shoe shop*
22 *crackling fire*   24 *small dog*
25–30 As a general rule (although there are exceptions), if the root word looks like a whole word, the suffix will most likely be '-able'; if the root word does not look like a whole word, the suffix will most likely be '-ible'.
25 **chargeable**
26 **irresistible**
27 **convertible** An exception to the rule.
28 **extendable**
29 **regrettable**
30 **avoidable**

TEST 12: Spelling (pages 24–25)

1–5 Pronunciations of *ough* include *through, rough, cough, thought, bough*. Other possible answers include *bought, borough, enough*.
6 **immediately**   7 **relevant**
8 **secretary**   9 **temperature**
10 **excellent**
11–22 The suffixes '-ant'/'-ance' and '-ent'/'-ence' are particularly difficult to work out as they are pronounced the same and there is no hard and fast rule to distinguish between them. If a root word can use '-ation' as a suffix, then '-ant'/'-ance' are most likely used.
11 **appearance**
12 **elegance**
13 **radiance** As per rule (radi<u>ation</u>).
14 **occurrence**
15 **silence**
16 **experience**
17 **pleasant**
18 **hesitant** As per rule (hesit<u>ation</u>).
19 **magnificent**
20 **abundant**
21 **stagnant** As per rule (stagn<u>ation</u>).
22 **transparent**
23–29 Refer to definition of root word in key words on page 47.
23 **garden**
24 **ornament**
25 **resist**
27 **shine**
28 **happy**
29 **alter**
30 **giraffe**
31 **pulley**

32 **grammar**
33 **professor**
34 **necessary**
35 **wrapping**
36–40 In '-fer' root word endings, when the second syllable is stressed (once the suffix has been added), the last 'r' is doubled. When the first syllable is stressed, the root word spelling remains the same.
36 **preferring**
37 **referral**
38 **preference**
39 **transferred**
40 **referring**

TEST 13: Comprehension (pages 26–27)

1 **pedigree** (lines 1–2)
2 *they are traditionally bred to work* (lines 9–11)
3 **plenty of exercise** (lines 19–20)
4 **when both parents are known** (section 2 lines 7–8)
5 *Cross-bred dogs are cheaper to buy, stronger in constitution and less highly strung* (section 2 lines 4, 12 and 13)
6 *mixed ancestry – a mix of different dog breeds* (section 3 line 1)
7 *it's hard to predict accurately how they will develop since their sires are unknown* (section 2 lines 5–7)
8 Child's own answer, for example, mongrel dogs because most of them make affectionate companions (section 3 line 3)
9 *offspring*
10 *sturdy*

TEST 14: Mixed (pages 28–29)

1 **bushes** Refer to Test 2 Spelling Q21.
2 **athletes** Refer to Test 2 Spelling Q24.
3 **convoys** Refer to Q2.
4 **motifs** Refer to Test 1 Mixed Q1 (this is an exception).
5 **kangaroos** Refer to Q2.
6 **babies** For words ending in 'y', change the 'y' to 'i' and add 'es'.
7–9 Refer to definition of mnemonic in key words on page 47. Child's own answers, e.g. unnecessary = *using new napkins eight children eat sugary sweets and raspberry yoghurts*.
10–14 Refer to Test 10 Sentences Q6–9.
10–11 Grandad, who was feeling grumpy anyway, got really cross when the puppy chewed his new slippers.

12–13 Take a few moments to listen to different sounds – perhaps the sound of the wind howling, sirens screaming, leaves rustling or buzzing planes.
14 To be able to understand your own beliefs and values, you need to learn about the beliefs and values of others.
15–24 A suffix is a group of letters added to the end of a root word to make a new word. Here are some possible answers.
15–16 *friendly, friendship*
17–18 *shameful, shameless*
19–20 *happiness, happily*
21–22 *painful, painless*
23–24 *greatness, greatly*
25 A colon is often used before a list or quotation – the first clause must be independent. For example: *We have two types of tree in our garden: beech and oak.*
26 A semicolon can be used to join two clauses, often related, together. For example: *It's snowing; I'm so excited.*
27–30 A semicolon can also be used to list expanded noun phrases. For example: *People enjoy summer for a number of reasons: it's warm; they enjoy doing things outside; they can eat BBQs; it stays light late into the evening.*

TEST 15: Vocabulary (pages 30–31)

1–5 Child's own sentences. Five sentences containing the listed words.
6 **husband**   7 **prince**
8 **nephew**   9 **gentleman** or **lord**
10 **lion**   11 **fox**
12–15 **television, DVD player, astronaut, website.** Children can work this out by choosing the nouns that identify modern inventions, occupations or ideas.
16–20 Refer to definition of abbreviation in key words on page 47.
16 **compact disc**
17 **kilogram**
18 **United States of America**
19 **South East or Stock Exchange**
20 **Member of Parliament or Military Police**
21–22 Possible answers include *outfit, outlaw*
23–24 Possible answers include *thrill, throne*
25–26 Possible answers include *disgrace, dispatch*
27–30 Refer to definition of metaphor in key words on page 47. Here are some possible answers:
27 *The wind was a howling beast.*
28 *The snow is soft balls of cotton wool.*
29 *The leaves are a prickly carpet.*
30 *His bedroom was a tip!*

TEST 16: Mixed (pages 32–33)

1–8 Refer to Test 7 Grammar Q1–8. Possible answers include *man* (common noun), *Lucy* (proper noun), *appearance* (abstract noun), *bunch* (collective noun).

9–12 Direct speech is written in inverted commas (speech marks) and is often followed or preceded by a reporting clause so the reader knows who has spoken (e.g. 'said Mum', or 'I whispered').

9 **"Ben, it is time to put the chips in the oven," called Mum.** 'It is' may be written as 'it's'.

10 **"There's nothing to worry about," said the vet.** 'Said the vet' may be replaced with 'the vet told me'.

11 **"It's time for lunch," announced Mrs Owen.** 'It's' may be written as 'it is'.

12 **"Rupesh, would you like to stay the night at my house?" asked Ryan.** This could also be written as *"Would you like to stay the night at my house?" Ryan asked Rupesh.*

13 As this is not hyphenated (like man-eating shark), 'man' must be used as a noun, e.g. *Man eating shark shocks local villagers*.

14 As this is hyphenated, the phrase must be used to show a bottle holding hot-water, rather than a hot (temperature) water bottle, e.g. *Sarah felt ill so she made herself a hot-water bottle*.

15 As this is not hyphenated, this word must be used to mean finding something or returning to health, as opposed to covering something again (re-cover), e.g. *If I get some rest, I may recover*.

16 As this is hyphenated, the phrase must be used to identify the manager of a small business, rather than a business manager who is small, e.g. *Anshul was a successful small-business manager*.

17 As this is not hyphenated, the phrase must be used to show a metal detector that is heavy, rather than something that detects heavy metals, e.g. *I felt so weak that I couldn't carry my heavy metal detector*.

18–22 Refer to definition of simile in key words on page 47. Here are some possible answers.

18 *The water was as blue as sapphire.*

19 *The swan was as white as snow.*

20 *The drum was as loud as a thunder clap.*

21 *Jo saw a spider that was as big as a house.*

22 *The monkey sat as quiet as a mouse.*

23–30 Refer to definition of root word in key words on page 47.

23 **marine** The prefix 'sub' has been added.

24 **claim** The prefix 'ex' has been added.

25 **post** The suffix 'age' has been added.

26 **digest** The suffix 'ible' has been added.

27 **rely** The suffix 'able' has been added.

28 **nation** The prefix 'inter' and suffix 'al' has been added.

29 **hygiene** The suffix 'ic' has been added.

30 **offence** The suffix 'ive' has been added.

TEST 17: Grammar (pages 34–35)

1–10 Refer to definition of adverb in key words on page 47. Here are some possible answers.

1–2 *ran quickly*

3–4 *worked slowly*

5–6 *searched helplessly*

7–8 *sat patiently*

9–10 *talked quietly*

11–15 Refer to definition of conjunction in key words on page 47. Child's own answers, e.g. Molly loved her party dress <u>because</u> it had pockets or <u>but</u> hated her shoes, etc.

16–20 Refer to definition of adjectival phrase in key words on page 47. Here are some possible answers.

16 *an unusually large banana*

17 *the extremely naughty children*

18 *a scary black spider*

19 *the surprisingly calm wind*

20 *a really exciting computer game*

21–30 Refer to definitions of abstract noun, preposition, pronoun and superlative on page 47. Possible answers include:

21–22 *friendship, hatred*

23–24 *above, under*

25–26 *(to) sit, (to) laugh*

27–28 *it, he*

29–30 *smallest, largest*

TEST 18: Comprehension (pages 36–37)

1 **The Second World War** (para 2 lines 1–3)

2 *He let him win at marbles; he lent him his wicket keeper's gloves; he gave him his best stamp* (para 4 lines 6–8)

3 *when he arrived at school with grazed knees, dirt on his blazer and red eyes from crying* (para 4 lines 13–15)

4 *because the boy's father was an electrician rather than being at the front line* (para 5 lines 11–13)

5 Child's own answer, for example, *because he didn't stand up for his dead father or defend his honour*

6 **He worked in a button factory** (para 7 lines 2–3)

7 Child's own answer, for example, *He might have felt like he was being strong and tough*.

8 *He was hiding his embarrassment about the fact that his father hadn't gone off to fight in the war.*

9 Child's own answer

10 *Most men were going off to fight in the war, and those who died were thought of as heroes.*

TEST 19: Mixed (pages 38–39)

1–4 Refer to Test 1 Mixed Q15–19.

1 *Two people can be more successful at doing something than one person.*

2 *You get better at something with practice.*

3 *If you help me, I will help you.*

4 *It is best not to change things.*

5–11 **"Can I open my present now?" asked Gina. "I have waited a very long time!"**

12–16 **"Let's go ice-skating," suggested Jenny.** An exclamation mark may be used instead of a comma.

17–22 Refer to definition of onomatopoeic in key words on page 47. Possible answers include:

17–18 *crash, whoosh*

19–20 *hissing, slithering*

21–22 *whizz, fizzle*

23 **pronoun**

24 **conjunction**

25 **adverb**

26 **verb or noun** *I hate eggs* or *The cat hissed with hate.*

27 **verb**

28–30 Refer to Test 6 Mixed Q9–14. Child's own answers.

TEST 20: Sentences (pages 40–41)

1–5 The verb *was* follows the subject when it is a singular noun; when it is plural, the verb *were* should be used instead.

1 **was or were** 'Family' is a collective noun and can be considered either singular or plural.

2 **was** 'The ball' is singular.

3 **were** 'Children' is plural.

4 **was** 'The villain' is singular.

5 **was** 'Hannah' is singular.

6–8 Refer to definitions of phrase and clause in key words on page 47. Child's own answers, for example, *The horses, <u>tired and hungry</u>, waited for their morning feed.* 'Tired and hungry' is a phrase as it does not contain a main verb.

9–10 Refer to definition of relative clause in key words on page 47. Child's own answers, for example, *The girl, who had long blonde hair, sat on a chair*.

11–15 "Quieten down!" bellowed the headteacher.

16–18 Darren raced towards the ball, not wanting to be beaten by anyone.

19–23 "Are we going to win?" called Helen.

24–26 In an active sentence, the subject is doing something ('The boy rode the horse.'). In a passive sentence, the subject is having something done to it ('The horse was ridden by the boy.'). A passive sentence often uses the word 'was' before the verb. Child's own answers, for example, *The dog was being walked by the boy.*

27 **D**ave's cats, **B**atman and **R**obin, tore up his **H**arry **P**otter poster.

28 **T**he train was late, eventually arriving in **M**anchester after **M**anchester **U**nited had won their match!

Puzzle 1 (page ㊷)

1 **South Africa**
2 **department store**
3 **Downing Street**
4 **pencil crayon**
5 **shopping trolley**
6 **Prince William**
7 **swimming costume**
8 **Blue Peter**

A and B Child's own answers

Puzzle 2 (page ㊸)

A 'soft c' is the letter 'c' pronounced as a s sound; a 'soft g' is the letter 'g' pronounces as a j sound. Soft cs and gs often precede the letters 'i', 'y' or 'e'.

necessary, innocent, receive, decision gaol, religion, vegetable, imagination

Puzzle 3 (page **44**)

Word families are those formed from the same root word (see p47 for a definition of root word). Here are some possible answers.

happy – happily, happiest, unhappy
phone – telephone, microphone, phoneme
question – questioning, questionable, questioned
detect – detective, detecting, detectable
graph – telegraph, autograph, photograph

Puzzle 4 (page **45**)

Child's own answers

Puzzle 5 (page **46**)

Across
   2 **bicycle**   5 **octopus**
   3 **triathlon**   6 **decade**
Down
   1 **octagon**
   4 **tripod**

Write the *root word* of each of these words.

23 gardener   _____

24 ornamental   _____

25 resistance   _____

26 noticeable   _____

27 shiny   _____

28 happiness   _____

29 alteration   _____

Add the missing double letters to each of these words.

30 gira__ __e   33 profe__ __or

31 pu__ __ey   34 nece__ __ary

32 gra__ __ar   35 wra__ __ing

Complete these word sums. Watch out for the spelling changes!

36 prefer + ing =   _____

37 refer + al =   _____

38 prefer + ence =   _____

39 transfer + ed =   _____

40 refer + ing =   _____

Read this extract carefully.

Pedigree or mongrel?

Pedigree dogs

Pedigree, or pure-bred, dogs are the most expensive to buy, but it is not usually difficult to find homes for their puppies. Being highly bred may make them more delicate than dogs of mixed ancestry and more likely to inherit defects. The very fact that they are descended from a line of dogs used traditionally for a particular form of work may make some of them unsuitable as pets for the average household. Dalmatians, for instance, were once carriage dogs. A pair of them would run alongside the horses in the capacity of outriders. Their elegant proportions and attractive, spotted coats mean they are now in demand as pets, but they should only be kept if they can be allowed plenty of exercise.

Cross-bred dogs

Cross-breds are the **progeny** of two pure-bred parents of different breeds. Cross-breds usually make very good pets. They are cheaper to buy, but of course cost as much to keep as pedigree dogs. When both parents are known, it is possible to estimate the adult size and type of cross-bred puppy. Depending on the combination of the parents' characteristics, a cross-bred dog can be very attractive, and may be stronger in constitution and often less highly strung than either of its parents.

Mongrel dogs

Mongrels are dogs of mixed ancestry. They are inexpensive and most make affectionate companions. Nearly all mongrels are **robust**, but since their sires are often unknown, it is impossible to predict accurately how mongrel puppies will develop. This is one reason why mongrels are difficult to home, and why so many are taken to animal welfare societies, such as the RSPCA, from which they can sometimes be adopted.

The Official RSPCA Pet Guide
Care for Your Dog

Answer these questions about the extract.

1   Which type of dog is most expensive to buy?

_____

2   Why are some pedigree dogs unsuitable to keep as pets for the average household?

_____

3   If a Dalmatian is kept as a pet what does it particularly need?

_____

4   When is it possible to estimate the adult size of a cross-bred dog?

_____

5   Write three differences between pedigree and cross-bred dogs.

_____

_____

6   Describe the parents of a mongrel dog.

_____

7   Why are some mongrel dogs difficult to home?

_____

8   Which type of dog would you choose to keep and why?

_____

_____

9   What is meant by the word **'progeny'**?

_____

10   What does **'robust'** mean?_____

Total

Test time: 0 |||||| 5 |||||| 10 minutes

Write each of these nouns in its plural form.

1   bush   _____

2   athlete   _____

3   convoy   _____

4   motif   _____

5   kangaroo   _____

6   baby   _____

Write a *mnemonic* to help you remember how to spell each of these words.

7   accommodate

    _____

8   government

    _____

9   unnecessary

    _____

Add the missing commas to these sentences.

10–11   Grandad who was feeling grumpy anyway got really cross when the puppy
        chewed his new slippers.

12–13   Take a few moments to listen to different sounds – perhaps the sound of the
        wind howling sirens screaming leaves rustling or buzzing planes.

14   To be able to understand your own beliefs and values you need to learn
        about the beliefs and values of others.

Add two suffixes to each of these to make new words.

15–16   friend   _____   _____

17–18   shame   _____   _____

19–20   happy   _____   _____

21–22   pain   _____   _____

23–24   great   _____   _____

Write three sentences, one with a colon, one with a semicolon and one with a colon introducing a list using three semicolons.

25 _____

26 _____

27–30 _____

_____

_____

_____

Total

Test 15: **Vocabulary**

Test time: 0 | | | | | 5 | | | | 10 minutes

Write each of these words in a sentence.

withhold

1 _____

access

2 _____

opportunity

3 _____

persistence

4 _____

mischievous

5 _____

Write the masculine gender of each of these words.

6 wife   _____   9 lady   _____

7 princess   _____   10 lioness   _____

8 niece   _____   11 vixen   _____

Circle the words that have come into the English language since 1900.

12–15

chimney   television   box

pottery   DVD player   glass   astronaut

bicycle   website   mantelpiece

Write these *abbreviations* in full.

16 CD _____

17 kg _____

18 USA _____

19 SE _____

20 MP _____

Fill the gaps with two words. The four words in each set need to be in alphabetical order.

21–22   outback   _____   _____   outsider

23–24   thread   _____   _____   thrush

25–26   disease   _____   _____   distress

Write a *metaphor* for each of these subjects.

27 wind

_____

28 snow

_____

29 leaves

_____

30 bedroom

_____

Total

List the four different types of noun. Write an example of each.

1–2 _____ noun   Example: _____

3–4 _____ noun   Example: _____

5–6 _____ noun   Example: _____

7–8 _____ noun   Example: _____

Write these sentences as *direct speech*.

9   Mum called to Ben that it was time to put the chips in the oven.

_____

10   The vet told me there was nothing to worry about.

_____

11   Mrs Owen announced it was time for lunch.

_____

12   Ryan asked Rupesh if he would like to stay the night at his house.

_____

_____

Write five sentences. In each sentence use the listed word or phrase correctly.

13   man eating shark _____

14   hot-water bottle _____

15   recover _____

16   small-business manager _____

17   heavy metal detector _____

Write a *simile* using the following subjects.

18   water

_____

19   swan

_____

20   drum

_____

21   spider

_____

22   monkey

_____

Write the *root word* of each of these words.

23   submarine   _____

24   exclaim   _____

25   postage   _____

26   digestible   _____

27   reliable   _____

28   international   _____

29   hygienic   _____

30   offensive   _____

TEST 17: **Grammar**

Test time: 0 ... 5 ... 10 minutes

Add a different verb and *adverb* to each sentence.

1–2   Fiona _____ _____ to the other side of the playground.

3–4   The postman _____ _____ in the rain.

5–6   The abandoned dog _____ _____ for his home.

7–8   The bird _____ _____ on her eggs waiting for them to hatch.

9–10   Mrs Seal's class _____ _____ as they waited for lunch.

Complete these sentences. Use a *conjunction* from the box in each one. You may use each word only once.

because	but	if	when	and

11   Molly loved her party dress _____

_____

12   Reuben had saved his pocket money for weeks _____

_____

13   Bill and Jake planned to meet in town _____

_____

14   The snake watched the mouse _____

_____

15   The sheep escaped from their field _____

_____

34

Write an *adjectival phrase* about each of these nouns.

16   a banana

_____

17   the children

_____

18   a spider

_____

19   the wind

_____

20   a computer game

_____

Write two examples of each of the following.

21–22   abstract noun   _____   _____

23–24   preposition   _____   _____

25–26   verb   _____   _____

27–28   pronoun   _____   _____

29–30   superlative adjective   _____   _____

Total

Read this extract carefully.

Hurricane Summer *by Robert Swindells*

Funny things, friendships. They tend to come and go, but most people have a special friend who stands out among all the others. I'm lucky – I've got two. One of them's been dead a long time now, but it doesn't matter – he'll always be my friend. As for the other ... well, as I said, friendships are funny. Best thing I can do is tell you about them.

The Second World War was on and I was ten. I was an only child. My dad had been killed the previous autumn serving with the Navy. Mum said I must always remember that my dad had been a hero, and I knew he had, that was the trouble.

You see, I wasn't a hero. Far from it.

There was this lad at school. Clive Simcox. He was the same age as me – we were in the same class – but Clive was taller and heavier, and for some reason that summer he started picking on me. I didn't like fighting so I was forever trying to please him. I let him win at marbles and lent him my wicket keeper's gloves. I even gave him my best stamp – a Guadeloupe triangular – but it was no use. He'd still ambush me on the way home from school and bash me up. He used to wait for me in the mornings too, and trip me as I ran past. I'd arrive at school with grazed knees and dirt on my blazer and red eyes from crying, and everybody would know Clive had had another go at me.

He used to make remarks about my Dad, which was even worse. Before the war Dad had been an electrician, so they made him an electrician in the Navy. I don't know what his work was exactly, but it had to do with electrical circuits and that sort of thing. Anyway, Clive had latched on to this and sometimes he'd say, "He **was nothing special**, you know, your dad. He wasn't a gunner or a torpedo man. He didn't kill any Germans. He was just an electrician, mending fuses and changing lightbulbs while other fellows did the fighting." This would be in the playground or on the street and he'd say it at the top of his voice so everyone could hear, and all the time he'd be pushing me – shoving me in the chest so that I had to keep stepping backwards. He was goading me of course – trying to make me fight, but I was too scared. Red-faced with shame, I'd retreat till he got bored and went off to bother somebody else.

I **despised** myself. I'd think, what sort of kid doesn't stick up for his dead father? Defend his honour? If I was half the hero Dad was, I'd stand up to Simcox and punch him on the nose, even if he bashed me up after ... When it came to it – when he was actually there in front of me with his red face and mocking eyes – I'd either try to run or let him hit me to get it over. I was ashamed of myself but I couldn't help it.

Funniest thing was, Simcox senior wasn't even in the forces. He worked in a button factory, but I daren't bring that up when Clive was tormenting me. Shows how scared I was, and believe me it's no joke being a coward when the world seems **full of heroes**.

1   In which war had the boy's father died? _____

2   List the three ways the boy tried to please Clive Simcox.

    _____

    _____

3   How did everyone know when Clive had bullied the boy?

    _____

4   Why did Clive Simcox believe the boy's father **'was nothing special'**?

    _____

5   In your own words describe why the boy **'despised'** himself.

    _____

6   What did Clive Simcox's dad do during the war?

    _____

7   How do you think Clive Simcox felt while bullying the boy?

    _____

    _____

8   Why do you think Clive Simcox was a bully?

    _____

    _____

9   When you see someone being bullied how do you feel?

    _____

    _____

10 Why did the world seem **'full of heroes'**?

    _____

    _____

Total

Write the meaning of each of these proverbs.

1 Two heads are better than one.

_____

_____

2 Practice makes perfect.

_____

_____

3 You scratch my back and I'll scratch yours.

_____

_____

4 Let sleeping dogs lie.

_____

_____

Rewrite these sentences with the missing punctuation.

5–11 Can I open my present now asked Gina I have waited a very long time

_____

_____

12–16 Lets go ice-skating suggested Jenny

_____

_____

Write two *onomatopoeic* words that can describe each of these.

17–18   an avalanche   _____   _____

19–20   a snake   _____   _____

21–22   a firework   _____   _____

What parts of speech are each of these words?

23   it   _____

24   but   _____

25   grumpily   _____

26   hate   _____

27   remove   _____

Write an example of each of the following.

28   a question

_____

29   a statement

_____

30   a command

_____

Total

TEST 20: **Sentences**

Test time: 0   5   10 minutes

Add 'was' or 'were' to each sentence to make it correct.

1 The Jacob family _____ relieved to reach their holiday home.

2 The dog barked excitedly every time the ball _____ thrown to him.

3 Mrs Trevis's children _____ very well-behaved during the concert.

4 Half the audience cheered when the villain _____ caught.

5 Hannah _____ too excited to sleep.

Complete each sentence with a *phrase* or *clause*.

6 The horses _____

_____ waited for their morning feed.

7 Ben rode his bike _____

_____ to Tuhil's house.

8 Rebecca _____

_____ waited for her brother.

Write two sentences that include a *relative clause*.

9 _____

10 _____

Rewrite these sentences correctly.

11–15 quieten down bellowed the headteacher

_____

16–18 darren raced towards the ball not wanting to be beaten by anyone

_____

_____

19–23 are we going to win called Helen

_____

_____

Write three sentences using the passive voice. Remember, a sentence is written in the passive voice when the subject of the sentence has an action done to it by someone or something else.

24 _____

25 _____

26 _____

Circle the letters in these sentences that need capitals.

27 dave's cats, batman and robin, tore up his harry potter poster.

28 the train was late, eventually arriving in manchester after manchester united had won their match!

Puzzle

In each of these groups of letters there are two words muddled together but with the letters placed in the correct order.

Can you sort the muddled words?

All capital letters are missing. Use the clues to help.

1 asfroiutcha
(a country)
_____   _____

2 sdtepoarrtmenet
(a type of shop)
_____   _____

3 dsotwrneientg
(a place in London)
_____   _____

4 crpeanciylon
(can be used to mark paper)
_____   _____

5 strhooppllienyg
(used in a supermarket)
_____   _____

6 wprirlnlicame
(a famous person)
_____   _____

7 csoswitmumimnge
(needed when doing the crawl or breaststroke)
_____   _____

8 bpeltueer
(a television programme)
_____   _____

Write some muddled words and clues of your own.
Try them out on someone.

A _____

_____

B _____

_____

Puzzle ❷

Find four soft c and four soft g words in this wordsearch.

b	k	r	e	c	e	i	v	e	v
n	d	g	n	s	t	m	d	f	e
e	g	a	o	l	f	a	c	n	g
c	x	k	c	a	k	g	o	g	e
e	r	e	l	i	g	i	o	n	t
s	a	d	b	t	s	n	b	s	a
s	f	d	n	i	d	a	d	n	b
a	n	s	c	b	s	t	n	t	l
r	c	e	t	o	z	i	m	b	e
y	d	o	g	n	d	o	c	g	a
i	n	n	o	c	e	n	t	o	k

Write the words you have found.

soft c words

_____

_____

_____

_____

soft g words

_____

_____

_____

_____

Puzzle ❸

How many words can you find from the same word family?

spark	happy	phone
spark**ler**	_____	_____
spark**ling**	_____	_____
spark**le**	_____	_____
_____	_____	_____
_____	_____	_____

question	detect	graph
_____	_____	_____
_____	_____	_____
_____	_____	_____
_____	_____	_____

Puzzle 4

As time passes more and more words are being invented.

For example the word 'cheeseburger' was invented to describe a hamburger that had cheese added to it.

Invent your own words for:

a hovering skateboard   _____

a jam and ham sandwich   _____

someone who always walks backwards   _____

an animal that speaks   _____

someone who can fly   _____

a pot plant that asks for water when it needs it   _____

Invent three more words with your own definitions.

_____

_____

_____

Puzzle ⑤

Complete the crossword.

Each of the answers begins with a number prefix.
The clues will help you!

Across

2   A two-wheeled vehicle.

3   A race in three parts.

5   An underwater animal with eight tentacles.

6   Ten years.

Down

1   A shape with eight sides.

4   A stand often used with a camera.

Key words

abbreviation	a word that has been shortened
abstract noun	a noun referring to a concept or idea, e.g. love, beauty
adjectival phrase	a group of words describing a noun
adjective	a word that describes somebody or something
adverb	a word that gives extra meaning to a verb
adverbial phrase	a word or phrase that makes the meaning of a verb, adjective or another adverb more specific, e.g. The Cheshire cat vanished *quite slowly*, beginning with the end of its tail
antonym	a word with a meaning opposite to another word, e.g. hot/cold
clause	a section of a sentence with a verb
collective noun	a noun referring to a group or collection of things, e.g. a swarm of bees
comparative	describes the amount of something (adverb or adjective), e.g. more, bigger
conjunction	a word used to link sentences, phrases or words, e.g. and, but
contraction	two words shortened into one with an apostrophe placed where the letter/s have been dropped, e.g. do not/don't
diminutive	a word implying smallness, e.g. duckling
fronted adverbial	an adverbial that has been moved before the verb, e.g. *The day after tomorrow*, I'm going on holiday
homophone	a word that has the same sound as another but a different meaning or spelling, e.g. right/write
idiom	a phrase that is not meant literally
infinitive	the basic form of the verb, e.g. to scream
indirect speech	what has been said without using the exact words or inverted commas
metaphor	a figurative expression in which something is described in terms usually associated with something else, e.g. the sky is a sapphire sea
mnemonic	a way of aiding the memory, e.g. a rhyme or silly story
modal verb	verbs that change the meaning of other verbs, e.g. can, will
onomatopoeic	a word that echoes a sound, associated with its meaning, e.g. hiss
parenthesis	this is a word or phrase that is separated off from the main sentence by brackets, commas or dashes usually because it contains additional information not essential to its understanding
phrase	a group of words that do not contain both a subject and a verb
preposition	a word that links nouns and pronouns to other parts of a sentence, e.g. he sat *behind* the door
pronoun	a word that can be used instead of a noun
relative clause	a special type of subordinate clause that makes the meaning of a noun more specific, e.g. The prize *that I won* was a book
root word	a word to which a prefix or suffix can be added to make another word, e.g. quick – *quick*ly
simile	an expression to describe what something is like, e.g. as cold as ice
superlative	describes the limit of a quality (adjective or adverb), e.g. most, least, shortest
synonym	a word with a very similar meaning to another word, e.g. quick/fast

Progress Grid

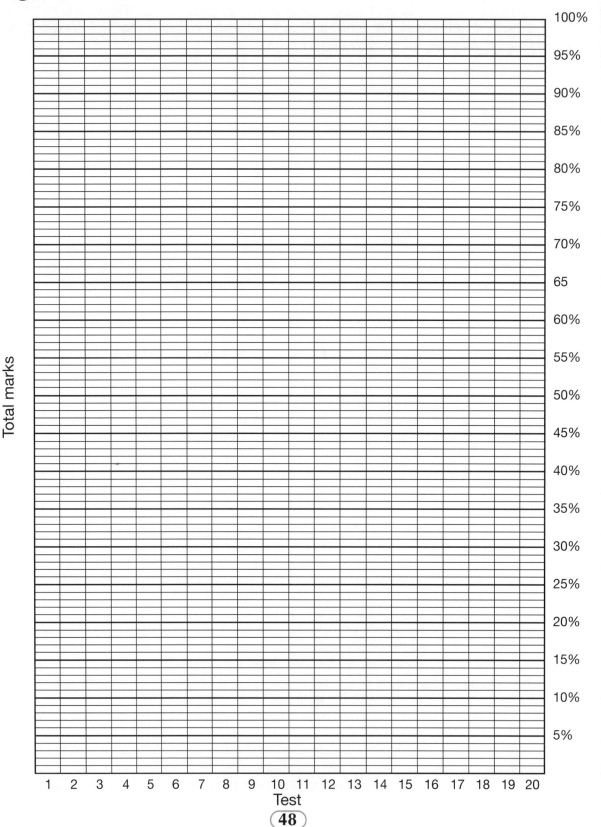

Total marks

Test

Maths

10 Minute Tests

10-11+ years

OXFORD

UNIVERSITY PRESS

1

What fraction of 2 hours is 15 minutes?
Circle the answer.

$\frac{1}{4}$ $\frac{1}{2}$ $\frac{2}{15}$ $\frac{1}{8}$ $\frac{1}{3}$

2

A 24-hour digital clock shows:

What would the time be if it were shown
on a 12-hour clock?
Circle the answer.

A 9.42   **B** 9.42 am   **C** 9.42 pm

D 12.42 pm   **E** 8.42 pm

3

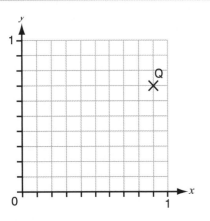

What are the coordinates of Q?
Circle the answer.

A (0.7, 0.9)   **B** (0.9, 0.7)   **C** (1.9, 0.7)

D (1.7, 0.9)   **E** (0.5, 0.6)

4

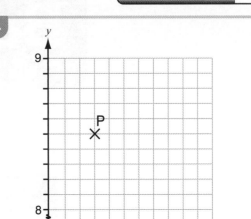

Using the grid, write down the coordinates
of P.

_____

5

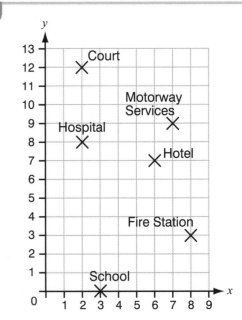

Where is the hotel?

_____

6

Give the coordinates of the train station.

(_____ , _____)

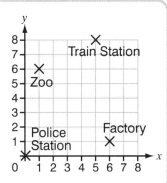

7

Which of the following options correctly lists the coordinates of all three points?

Circle the answer.

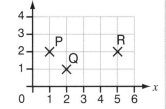

A P(1, 2)   Q(2, 1)   R(5, 2)

B P(2, 1)   Q(1, 2)   R(2, 5)

C P(1, 2)   Q(1, 2)   R(5, 2)

D P(2, 1)   Q(2, 1)   R(5, 2)

E P(1, 2)   Q(2, 1)   R(2, 5)

8

What are the coordinates of the points R, S and T?

Circle the answer.

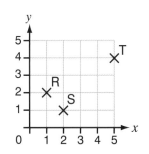

A R(1, 2)   S(2, 1)   T(4, 5)

B R(2, 1)   S(1, 2)   T(4, 5)

C R(1, 2)   S(2, 1)   T(5, 4)

D R(1, 1)   S(2, 1)   T(4, 5)

E R(1, 2)   S(1, 2)   T(5, 4)

9

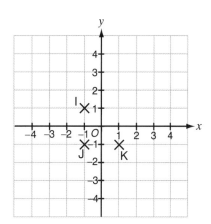

What are the coordinates of the points I, J and K?

Circle the answer.

A I(–1, 1)   J(1, 1)   K(1, –1)

B I(1, –1)   J(–1, –1)   K(–1, 1)

C I(–1, 1)   J(–1, –1)   K(–1, 1)

D I(1, –1)   J(–1, –1)   K(1, –1)

E I(–1, 1)   J(–1, –1)   K(1, –1)

10

A, B and D form three corners of a square. What are the coordinates of point C, which completes the square?

Circle the answer.

(2, –2)   (–2, 2)   (–2, –2)   (2, 2)   (2, 0)

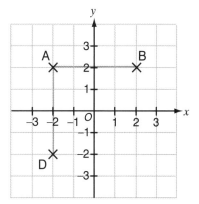

Total

TEST 2: **Number**

1 What is the number 59 038 in words?
Circle the answer.

A Fifty-nine thousand and thirty-eight

B Five hundred and ninety thousand and thirty-eight

C Fifty-nine thousand three hundred and eighty

D Five thousand nine hundred and thirty-eight

E Five hundred and nine thousand and thirty-eight

2 Ninety thousand nine hundred and nine.
Which answer shows this written as a number?
Circle the answer.

99 099   99 999   90 909
90 009   90 099

3 103 247
The 2 in this number is worth two hundred.
What is the three worth?
Circle the answer.

A Three hundred   **B** Thirty

C Three   **D** Thirty thousand

E Three thousand

4 Find a number for the blank space so that the list is in order of size.
2.35, 2.39, ..., 2.42
Circle the answer.

A 2.40   **B** 2.3   **C** 2.421

D 2.381   **E** 2.30

5 13, 130, ..., 13 000, 130 000
What should be the value of the 3 in the missing term?

_____

6 From the list find the smallest number.
Circle the answer.

7.6   7.06   7.60   7.006   7.600

7 In a class of 30 pupils, 11 are girls.
Approximately what proportion are boys?
Circle the most appropriate answer.

$\frac{1}{2}$ $\frac{11}{30}$ $\frac{1}{3}$ $\frac{2}{3}$ $\frac{5}{6}$

8 To make 2500 ml of orange squash, 500 ml of concentrate must be used.
What proportion of water must be used to make up the rest?
Circle the answer.

$\frac{1}{5}$ $\frac{1}{4}$ $\frac{4}{5}$ $\frac{3}{4}$ $\frac{2}{5}$

9 7.6324
What is this number to two decimal places?

_____

10 8.9956
What is this number to two decimal places?
Circle the answer.

9.00   8.99   8.90   9.0000   9.0056

Total _____

TEST 3: **Shape and Space**

1

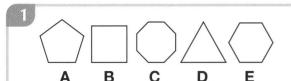

| A | B | C | D | E |

An angle inside a polygon is called an interior angle.

Which of the above polygons has the smallest interior angle?

Circle the answer.

2

Which of the following shapes has nine diagonals?

Circle the answer.

A Pentagon **B** Quadrilateral **C** Octagon

D Triangle **E** Hexagon

3

Which of these makes a word when rotated through 180°?

Circle the answer.

SIH   ISH   HIS   SHI   IHS

4

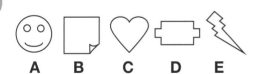

| A | B | C | D | E |

Which of these shapes has rotational symmetry?

Circle the answer.

5

Which of these does not have a vertical line of symmetry?

Circle the answer.

MUM   TAT   HAH   LAL   XOX

6

Which of these has a horizontal line of symmetry?

Circle the answer.

DID   CAT   HUH   NUN   TAT

7-8

What is the perimeter of each of the shapes below?

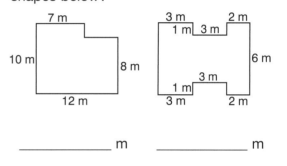

_____ m   _____ m

9

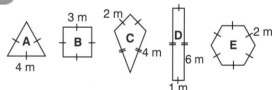

Which shape has a different perimeter from the others?

_____

10

What is the perimeter of this shape?

Circle the answer.

A $12a$ **B** a^{12} **C** $6a$

D $aaaaaa$ **E** a^6

Total

TEST 4: Data Handling

Test time: 0 5 10 minutes

1

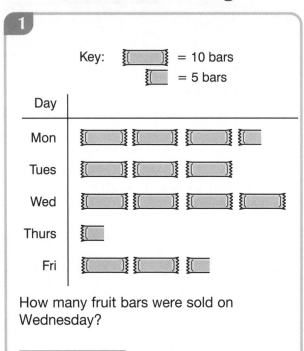

Key: = 10 bars
= 5 bars

Day	
Mon	
Tues	
Wed	
Thurs	
Fri	

How many fruit bars were sold on Wednesday?

_____

2

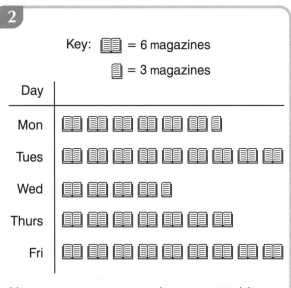

Key: = 6 magazines
= 3 magazines

Day	
Mon	
Tues	
Wed	
Thurs	
Fri	

How many more magazines were sold on Monday than on Wednesday?
Circle the answer.

A 12   **B** Can't tell   **C** 2
D $6\frac{1}{2}$ **E** 0

3

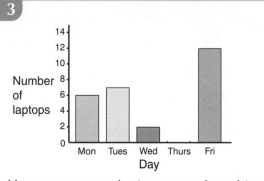

How many more laptops were bought on Friday than on Tuesday?

_____

4

How many more pupils prefer maths than geography?

_____

5

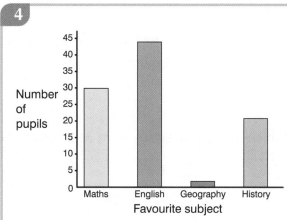

How many pupils completed more than 20 laps in a charity race?

_____

6

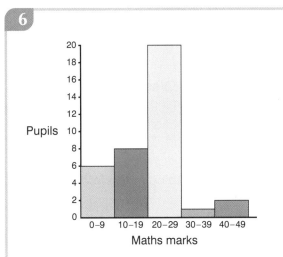

The pass mark for a maths test was 20.
How many pupils passed the test?

_____

7

A bag contains 2 red, 4 green and 6 yellow marbles. Lily picks a marble at random.

In which of the options below are both statements true? Circle the answer.

A You have an even chance of picking a yellow marble.
You have a greater than even chance of picking a red marble.

B You are certain to pick a marble.
You have a greater than even chance of picking a yellow marble.

C You have a less than even chance of picking a red marble.
You have a less than even chance of picking a green marble.

D You have a greater than even chance of picking a yellow marble.
You have a less than even chance of picking a green marble.

E You have a greater than even chance of picking a green marble.
You have an even chance of picking a yellow marble.

8

Jo rolls a fair dice numbered 1 to 6. In which of the options below are both statements true?
Circle the answer.

A You have an even chance of rolling an even number.
You are certain to roll a number less than six.

B You have an even chance of rolling a prime number.
You are certain to roll a number less than seven.

C You have a less than even chance of rolling an odd number.
You are certain to roll a number less than seven.

D You have a greater than even chance of rolling a prime number.
You are certain to roll a number less than five.

E You have a less than even chance of rolling a prime number.
You have an even chance of rolling an odd number.

9

A bag contains some coloured balls.

There are: 3 black, 2 red, 5 blue, 6 green and 7 yellow.

Ranjna picks a ball at random.

What is the chance that she doesn't pick a red ball?

_____

10

When Eric spins the spinner, what is the probability that it will land on a number greater than 1?

_____

Total

TEST 5: **Number**

1 1   8   9   15   16

Look at these numbers. Which is neither a square number nor a cube number?

Circle the answer.

2 1   2   9   16   25

Look at these numbers. Which is both a square number and a cube number?

Circle the answer.

3

Which option shows two prime numbers that add up to make a cube number?

Circle the letter.

A 3 and 5   **B** 1 and 7   **C** 2 and 6

D 5 and 120 **E** 4 and 12

4

Look at the pattern below:

Line 1   1 = 1
Line 2   1 + 3 = 4
Line 3   1 + 3 + 5 = 9
Line 4   1 + 3 + 5 + 7 = 16
Line 5   1 + 3 + 5 + 7 + 9 = 25

How many prime numbers would line 6 contain?

_____

5

Out of 567 people surveyed, 78 preferred curries, 206 preferred stir-fries and the rest preferred pasta.

How many liked pasta?

_____

6

127 children from Grassmoor Primary School are performing a show.

72 children are acting, 49 children are assisting backstage. The rest are helping in the front of house.

How many are helping in the front of house?

_____

7-8

The caterers at a concert make 728 meals.

Unfortunately 986 people turn up.

How many people go without a meal?

_____

If an extra 300 meals are made, how many are left over?

_____

9

A bus starts at the terminus. It stops three times before it reaches the airport.

35 people get on at the terminus.

14 people get on at the school, 2 get off.

12 get on at the hospital and 16 get off.

6 get on in the High St and 28 get off.

How many people are on the bus when it arrives at the airport?

_____

10

Sara buys some clothes worth £58.63.

As she spends over £50 she receives a £5 discount.

How much does she pay in total?

_____

8

Total

Test 6: Data Handling

1

25	27	26	27	25	24	25
24	26	27	28	30	30	27

The midday temperatures in °C recorded over a fortnight are shown above.

What is the mode?

_____ °C

2

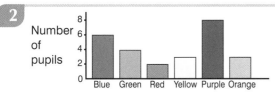

Number of pupils

Blue Green Red Yellow Purple Orange

This graph shows the favourite colours of Year 5.

What is the modal colour?

_____

3

Seven people's wages are listed below.

£110 £150 £120 £130 £140 £220 £435

What is the median wage?

Circle the answer.

A £143   **B** £435   **C** £186

D £140   **E** £130

4

The total attendance in one season for Cliffridge Football Club was 960 000.

They played 24 games.

What was the mean attendance?

_____

5

Month	May	June	July	Aug	Sep
Hours	174	186	191	199	188

Find the range for the hours of sunshine shown in the table above.

Circle the answer.

A 26   **B** 199   **C** 186   **D** 5   **E** 25

6

6   4   2   0   8

Find the range of the numbers above.

Circle the answer.

A 8   **B** 0   **C** 4   **D** 6   **E** 20

7

8   6   2   1   13

Find the range of the numbers above.

Circle the answer.

A 13   **B** 1   **C** 12   **D** 8   **E** 30

8

12   7   20   5   19

What is the median of these numbers?

Circle the answer.

A 20   **B** 12   **C** 62   **D** 7   **E** 19

9

Day	Mon	Tues	Wed	Thurs	Fri
No. of cups	2		8	9	4

Heather thinks her mum is drinking too many cups of coffee a day.

Heather asks her some questions and completes this table.

Her mum says her mean is 7.

How many cups did she drink on Tuesday?

_____

10

Day	Mon	Tues	Wed	Thurs	Fri
Hours	12	13	8		4

Ali's dad thinks Ali is spending too many hours playing games on the computer.

His dad asks Ali some questions and completes this table.

Ali's dad says his mean is 9.

How many hours did Ali play games on Thursday?

_____

Time for a break! Go to Puzzle Page 42   9   Total

TEST 7: **Shape and Space**

1

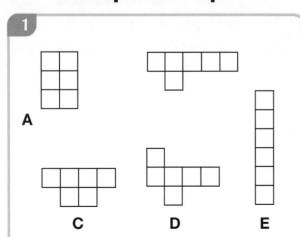

A

C   D   E

Look at the nets above.

Which one is the net of a closed cube?

Circle the answer.

2

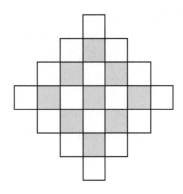

All squares measure 30 cm by 30 cm.

What is the area of the entire pattern in m²?

Circle the answer.

A 25.2 m²

B 2.52 m²

C 2520 m²

D 2.25 m²

E 22 500 m²

3

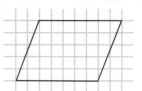

In the diagram above 1 square represents 1 cm².

What is the area of the parallelogram?

_____ cm²

4

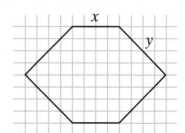

What is the correct formula for the area of this shape?

Circle the answer.

A $4x^2$ **B** $(x + y)^2$

C $2x^2y^2$ **D** $\frac{1}{2}xy$

E $2x^2 + 2y^2$

5

The side length of the smaller equilateral triangle is half the side length of the larger equilateral triangle.

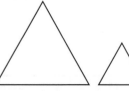

How many times will the smaller triangle fit into the larger triangle?

Circle the answer.

2   3   4   5   6

6

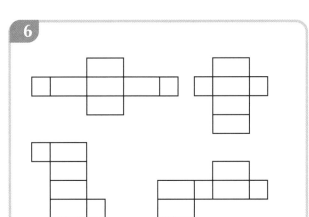

How many of the nets shown above will form a closed cuboid when folded?

Circle the answer.

A None of them

B Only 1 of them

C 2 of them

D 3 of them

E All of them

7

What is the area of the triangle shown?

13 cm   12 cm

4 cm

_____ cm²

8

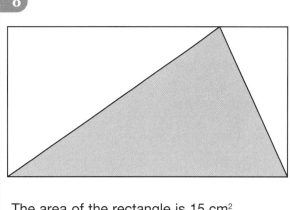

The area of the rectangle is 15 cm².

What is the area of the triangle?

_____ cm²

9

The area of a rectangle is 70 cm².

What could be the perimeter of the rectangle?

Circle the answer.

A 7 cm

B 9 cm

C 12 cm

D 26 cm

E 34 cm

10

The perimeter of a rectangle is 24 cm.

If the rectangle is 10 cm long, what is the area of the rectangle?

Circle the answer.

A 10 cm²

B 11 cm²

C 20 cm²

D 32 cm²

E 220 cm²

Total

TEST 8: **Number**

1

Which of the following has the smallest value?

Circle the answer.

$\frac{1}{2}$ $\frac{6}{10}$ $\frac{3}{5}$ $\frac{4}{9}$ $\frac{5}{8}$

2

Which of the following has the largest value?

Circle the answer.

$\frac{2}{5}$ 20% $\frac{1}{3}$ 35%   0.3

3

Which option is different from the others?

Circle the answer.

A $\frac{3}{4}$ of 200   **B** 75% of 200

C 0.75 of 200   **D** 0.5 of 400

E 150% of 100

4

Which option has the largest value?

Circle the answer.

A 62% of 60   **B** 0.63 of 60   **C** $\frac{3}{5}$ of 60

D $\frac{2}{3}$ of 60   **E** $\frac{5}{8}$ of 60

5

Jane scores 17 out of 25 in a maths test.
What percentage did she get?

_____

6

What percentage of the diagram is shaded?

_____

7

Rowan has 50 marbles.
He gives 13 to Jack and keeps the rest.
What percentage does he keep for himself?

_____

8

Ajay noticed that out of 400 buildings, 20% of them were terraced houses.
How many terraced houses are there?

_____

9

A sofa costs £1800.
During a sale the price is reduced by a third.
What is the sale price of the sofa?

_____

10

Out of 1400 dog owners surveyed, 8 out of 10 bought 'Doggy' dog food.
How many people bought other brands?

_____

Total _____

1-2

Below are 2 nets of open cuboids.
When each net is folded, it makes an open box.
What is the volume of each box?

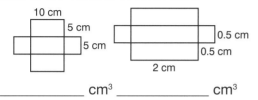

_____ cm³ _____ cm³

3

What number does the arrow point to in the scale?

_____

4

Tom buys three 2 litre bottles of water, 1.5 litres of milk and a 1 kg bag of potatoes.
What is the total weight of the shopping?
Circle the answer.

A 0.5 kg   **B** 2.5 kg   **C** 5.5 kg

D 8.5 kg   **E** 10.5 kg

5

The weight limit for airline luggage is 25 kg.
A case weighs 25.80 kg.
An item weighing 850 g is removed.
How much does the case now weigh?
Circle the answer.

A 24.95 kg   **B** 26.65 kg   **C** 25.95 kg

D −825.80 kg **E** 17.30 kg

6

A tree is about 6 times the height of a tall man who is standing next to it.
Circle the answer that would be the closest to the height of the tree.

A 50 m   **B** 2000 mm   **C** 40 cm

D 5 mm   **E** 12 m

7

Tim buys a medium-sized rucksack.
Approximately how many litres will it hold?
Circle the answer.

A 0.5 litres   **B** 5 litres   **C** 50 litres

D 500 litres   **E** 5000 litres

8

Which container will hold about 20 litres?
Circle the correct letter.

A a bath   **B** a sink   **C** a kettle

D a milk bottle   **E** an egg cup

9

What is the area of this shape?

_____ m²

10

The area of the shaded triangle is 1000 mm².
What is the area of the larger triangle?
Circle the answer.

A 90 000 mm² **B** 8000 mm² **C** 9.0 cm²

D 90 cm²   **E** 900 cm²

Total

TEST 10: **Number**

1

Out of 24 pairs of jeans, $\frac{2}{3}$ of them are blue.
How many pairs of jeans are blue?

_____

2

300 people are surveyed.
$\frac{2}{5}$ of them are 21 and under.
How many are 21 and under?

_____

3

250 people visit a coffee shop.
$\frac{3}{10}$ of the people order black coffee.
The rest order white coffee.
How many people order white coffee?

_____

4

200 flights leave Abbeytown airport in one day.
$\frac{4}{5}$ are domestic and the rest are international.
How many flights are international?

_____

5

In a 26-mile marathon, Gary sprints $\frac{1}{13}$ of the way, jogs $\frac{7}{13}$ of the way and walks the rest of the way.
How many miles does he walk for?

_____ miles

6

The journey time from Greentown to Greenberg normally takes 40 minutes.
Due to traffic congestion, journey times have increased by 15%.
What is the new journey time?

_____

7

Asima has £64.
She gives $\frac{1}{8}$ to Mary.
She gives $\frac{3}{8}$ to Jason.
The rest is given to Nabeel.
How much is Nabeel given?

_____

8

A shirt costs £30 before a '20% off everything' sale.
How much is the shirt in the sale?

_____

9

500 ml out of a 2.5 litre bottle of orange squash is concentrate.
What fraction is concentrate?
Circle the answer.

$\frac{1}{5}$ $\frac{1}{4}$ $\frac{1}{3}$ $\frac{1}{2}$ $\frac{1}{25}$

10

4 kg of a certain type of food contains 20 g of fat.
What fraction of the food is fat?

_____

14

Total _____

TEST 11: **Algebra**

1

I think of a number and multiply it by 4, then add 12. The answer I get is 76.
What number did I think of?

_____

2

Gary has 21 marbles.
He has x red marbles.
He has three more blue marbles than red.
He has four times as many green as red.
How many red marbles does he have?

_____

3

The numbers 1, 2, and 3 are consecutive.
Their sum is 1 + 2 + 3 = 6.
The sum of another set of three consecutive whole numbers is 21.
Find the smallest of these numbers.

_____

4

Linda has £3.60 and Mike has £4.80.
Mike gives Linda some 20p coins.
They then have the same amount of money.
How many 20p coins did Mike give Linda?

_____

5

$5x + 3y = 2z$
Find the value of z when $x = 5$ and $y = 3$.

_____

6

Akshay was x years old 5 years ago.
How old will he be in 7 years time?
Circle the answer.

A $x + 2$ **B** $x - 12$ **C** $12 - x$

D $12 + x$ **E** $x + 7$

7

y is $\frac{4}{5}$ of x.
Look at the list of statements below.
Circle the statement which is incorrect.

A $y = \frac{4}{5}x$ **B** $x = \frac{5}{4}y$ **C** $5y = 4x$

D $4y = 5x$ **E** $\frac{y}{x} = \frac{4}{5}$

8

A rectangle has a width x cm.
Its length is twice as long as its width.
Find an expression for the perimeter of the rectangle in terms of x.

_____

9

Minibuses have x seats. Coaches have y seats.
Bruce hires 2 minibuses and 7 coaches.
How many seats will there be in total?
Leave your answer in terms of x and y.

_____

10

If $7x - 9 = 10x - 18$, what is the value of x?

_____

15

Total

1

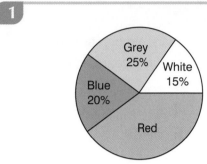

The are 700 cars in a car park.
How many cars are red?

_____

2

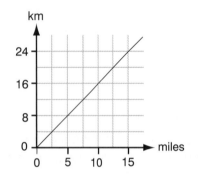

The graph shows the relationship between miles and kilometres.

Complete the following statement:

20 km is equivalent to _____ miles.

3

Alexander collected the following data from 100 pupils.

	Boys	Girls
Reggae	17	29
Hip Hop	13	7
Indipop	12	?

How many girls prefer Indipop music?

_____

4

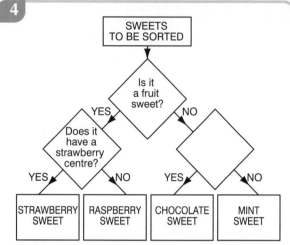

What is missing from the decision tree?
Circle the answer.

A Is it chocolate? **B** Is it mint?

C IT IS MINT. **D** IT IS CHOCOLATE.

E Is it not chocolate?

5

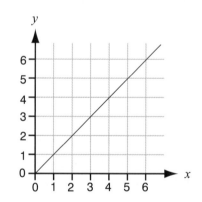

The end points of five lines are given below.
Which line is perpendicular to the line in the diagram?

Circle the answer.

A (1, 2) and (2, 2) **B** (1, 3) and (3, 3)

C (3, 1) and (1, 3) **D** (1, 4) and (4, 2)

E (5, 0) and (1, 3)

6

Bhavesh collected the following data from 100 pupils.

	Boys	Girls
English	19	7
Geography	4	?
Maths	38	30

How many girls preferred geography?

_____

7

A bag contains 8 red marbles, 2 green marbles and 10 black marbles.

You pick a marble at random from the bag.

In which of the options below are both statements true?

Circle the answer.

A You have a greater than even chance of picking a black marble.

You have a less than even chance of picking a green marble.

B You have an even chance of picking a black marble.

You have a greater than even chance of picking a red marble.

C You have a greater than even chance of picking a green marble.

You have an even chance of picking a black marble.

D You have a less than even chance of picking a red marble.

You have a less than even chance of picking a green marble.

E You are certain to pick a marble.

You have a greater than even chance of picking a black marble.

8

Key: ⟦▭⟧ = 10 bars   ⟦▭ = 5 bars

Day	
Mon	⟦▭⟧ ⟦▭⟧ ⟦▭⟧ ⟦▭
Tues	⟦▭⟧ ⟦▭⟧ ⟦▭
Wed	⟦▭⟧ ⟦▭⟧ ⟦▭⟧ ⟦▭⟧
Thurs	⟦▭
Fri	⟦▭⟧ ⟦▭⟧ ⟦▭

Look at the pictogram above.
How many fruit bars were sold during the whole week?

_____

9

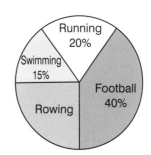

64 children were asked which sports they enjoyed.
How many children liked rowing?

_____

10

Look at this table showing the performance of the school cricket team.

Year	Won	Drawn	Lost
2002	7	8	5
2003	13	2	5
2004	6	10	4

How many matches in total did the team not lose?

_____

TEST 13: **Number**

1 A coach holds 52 passengers.
12 fully-occupied coaches are required to transport fans to a football match.
How many fans travel by coach?

_____

2 A crate can hold 24 cans.
Simon wants to order 312 cans.
How many crates should he order?

_____

3

A length of wood is 220 cm long.
It is cut into lengths of 30 cm.
How many complete pieces are made?

_____

4

2800 music fans attend a concert.
They travel in coaches. Each coach has 53 seats.
How many coaches are required?

_____

5

Pattern 1   Pattern 2   Pattern 3
How many tiles will be in Pattern 4?

_____

6

Circle the multiple of both 5 and 7.

A 12   **B** 57   **C** 14   **D** 35   **E** 15

7

Pattern 1   Pattern 2   Pattern 3

Pattern number	1	2	3	4
Grey tiles	1	2	3	
White tiles	8	10	12	
Total tiles	9	12	15	

Which option correctly completes the details for Pattern 4?
Circle the answer.

A Grey tiles = 4, White tiles = 12, total tiles = 16

B Grey tiles = 3, White tiles = 14, total tiles = 17

C Grey tiles = 4, White tiles = 12, total tiles = 17

D Grey tiles = 4, White tiles = 14, total tiles = 18

E Grey tiles = 4, White tiles = 14, total tiles = 16

8

A drummer beats his drum once every four seconds.
A second drummer beats his drum once every five seconds.
They both start at the same time.
After how many more seconds do they beat their drums together again?

_____

9

What is the smallest number divisible by both 8 and 12?

_____

10

What is the smallest number that is exactly divisible by 3 and 13?

_____

18

Total

TEST 14: Algebra

Test time: 0 5 10 minutes

1

$4a + 2b - 7c = d$.

Find the value of d when $a = 5$, $b = 2$ and $c = 3$.

____

2

$4a + 2b + 3c = 20$

Which of the statements below is incorrect?

Circle the answer.

A $8a + 4b + 6c = 40$

B $4a + 2b = 20 - 3c$

C $4a + 2b + 3c - 20 = 0$

D $4a + 2b + 4c = 20 + c$

E $4a = 20 + 2b - 3c$

3

? → [ ] → 168

This machine doubles and then adds 2.

Which number has been put in?

____

4

The length of a rectangle is 8 cm more than its width. Its width is x cm.

A square has a side length of y cm.

The perimeter of the rectangle is larger than that of the square.

How much bigger is the perimeter of the rectangle than that of the square?

Circle the answer.

A $2x + 8 - y$ **B** $4x + 16 - 4y$

C $8x - 4y$ **D** $8xy$ **E** $2x + 8 - 4y$

5

If $17 - 16x = 3 - 2x$, what is the value of x?

____

6

48 → [ ] → **?**

This machine divides by 3 and then multiplies by 6.

Which number comes out?

____

7

If $3x + 2 = 2x + 7$, what is the value of x?

____

8

If $32 - x = 23 + 2x$, what is the value of x?

____

9

If Rose had 18 more stamps, she would have four times as many as she actually has.

How many stamps does she have?

____

10

A father's age and his son's age add up to 64. The father is 36 years older than his son.

How old is his son?

____

Total

1–3

Guide the vehicles along the white squares from the start to the finish.

Each vehicle can only move FORWARD, TURN LEFT 90° and TURN RIGHT 90°.

1

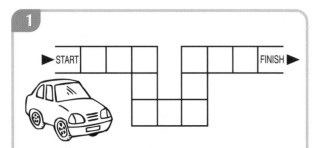

START | | | | | | | FINISH ▶

Circle the correct instructions.

A FORWARD 3, TURN LEFT 90°,
FORWARD 2, TURN RIGHT 90°,
FORWARD 2, TURN LEFT 90°,
FORWARD 2, TURN RIGHT 90°,
FORWARD 3

B FORWARD 3, TURN RIGHT 90°,
FORWARD 2, TURN LEFT 90°,
FORWARD 2, TURN LEFT 90°,
FORWARD 2, TURN RIGHT 90°,
FORWARD 3

C FORWARD 3, TURN RIGHT 90°,
FORWARD 2, TURN RIGHT 90°,
FORWARD 2, TURN LEFT 90°,
FORWARD 2, TURN RIGHT 90°,
FORWARD 3

D FORWARD 3, TURN RIGHT 90°,
FORWARD 2, TURN RIGHT 90°,
FORWARD 2, TURN RIGHT 90°,
FORWARD 2, TURN RIGHT 90°,
FORWARD 3

E FORWARD 3, TURN LEFT 90°,
FORWARD 2, TURN LEFT 90°,
FORWARD 2, TURN LEFT 90°,
FORWARD 2, TURN LEFT 90°,
FORWARD 3

2

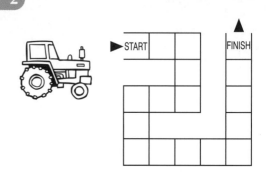

▶START | | FINISH

Circle the correct instructions.

A FORWARD 2, TURN RIGHT 90°,
FORWARD 2, TURN LEFT 90°,
FORWARD 2, TURN RIGHT 90°,
FORWARD 2, TURN LEFT 90°,
FORWARD 4, TURN LEFT 90°,
FORWARD 4

B FORWARD 2, TURN RIGHT 90°,
FORWARD 2, TURN RIGHT 90°,
FORWARD 2, TURN LEFT 90°,
FORWARD 2, TURN RIGHT 90°,
FORWARD 4, TURN LEFT 90°,
FORWARD 4

C FORWARD 2, TURN RIGHT 90°,
FORWARD 2, TURN RIGHT 90°,
FORWARD 2, TURN LEFT 90°,
FORWARD 2, TURN LEFT 90°,
FORWARD 4, TURN LEFT 90°,
FORWARD 4

D FORWARD 2, TURN RIGHT 90°,
FORWARD 2, TURN LEFT 90°,
FORWARD 2, TURN LEFT 90°,
FORWARD 2, TURN LEFT 90°,
FORWARD 4, TURN LEFT 90°,
FORWARD 4

E FORWARD 2, TURN LEFT 90°,
FORWARD 2, TURN RIGHT 90°,
FORWARD 2, TURN LEFT 90°,
FORWARD 2, TURN LEFT 90°,
FORWARD 4, TURN LEFT 90°,
FORWARD 4

3

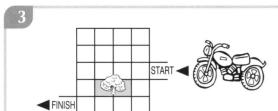

Circle the correct instructions.

A FORWARD 2, TURN LEFT 90°,
FORWARD 3, TURN RIGHT 90°,
FORWARD 1

B FORWARD 3, TURN LEFT 90°,
FORWARD 2, TURN RIGHT 90°,
FORWARD 2

C FORWARD 4, TURN LEFT 90°,
FORWARD 2, TURN RIGHT 90°,
FORWARD 1

D FORWARD 1, TURN LEFT 90°,
FORWARD 4, TURN RIGHT 90°,
FORWARD 1

E FORWARD 2, TURN LEFT 90°,
FORWARD 2, TURN RIGHT 90°,
FORWARD 3

4

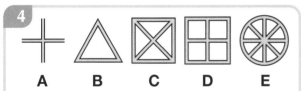

A papergirl does not want to visit the same street more than once.

She can pass over the same street corners.

On which housing estate is this possible?

Circle the answer.

5

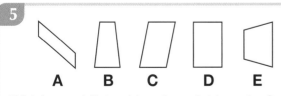

Which quadrilateral has four right angles?

Circle the answer.

6

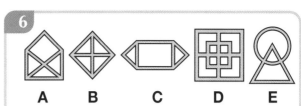

A postman does not want to visit the same street more than once.

He can pass over the same street corners.

On which housing estate is this possible?

Circle the answer.

7

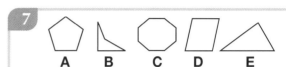

Which polygon has an internal reflex angle?

Circle the answer.

8

The diagram shows a rectangle joined to an equilateral triangle.

Find the size of the angle marked x.

_____ °

9

One of the angles of this scalene triangle is 30°.

The other angle is 80°.

Find the size of the third angle marked a.

_____ °

10

What is the approximate size of the angle marked b in this rhombus?

Circle the answer.

A 260° **B** 40° **C** 180° **D** 140° **E** 310°

Total

TEST 16: **Mixed**

Test time: 0 | | | | | 5 | | | | | 10 minutes

1

Given that $4x + 2y$ is the total cost in pounds for four adults and two children to enter a museum, which of the following statements is correct?

Circle the correct answer.

The cost for four adults and two children to enter the museum can also be written as:

A $8xy$ **B** $42xy$ **C** $6xy$

D $2(2x + y)$ **E** $8xy^2$

2

Which letter shows two prime numbers that add up to make a square number?

Circle the answer.

A 12 and 13 **B** 17 and 19 **C** 16 and 20

D 16 and 8 **E** 1 and 35

3

435 pupils are put into classes of 23 pupils. How many complete classes are there?

_____

4

If $6x + 7 = 28 - x$, what is the value of x?

_____

5

How many minutes are there in total in 4 hours and 32 minutes?

_____

6

Kevin wants to estimate the length of a room.

It takes him 15 strides to walk the length of the room.

What is the approximate length of the room?

Circle the answer.

A 40 m **B** 1400 mm **C** 1400 cm

D 200 cm **E** 3 km

7

The cost of a ham roll is £x and the cost of a tuna salad is £y.

Brian orders 5 ham rolls and 3 tuna salads.

What is a correct expression for the total cost of his order?

Circle the answer.

A $53xy$ **B** $5x + 3y$ **C** $15xy$

D $8xy$ **E** $15(x + y)$

8 Write in words the number 14 205.

_____

_____

9 4.3201

What is this number to two decimal places?

_____

10 14 9 22 7 21

These are the number of letters received by a library each day for a week.

What is the median number of letters?

_____

22

Total

Test time: 0   5   10 minutes

1

Here is part of a conversion table.
Which figure is missing from the table?

lbs	g	kg	lbs
5	2270	5	11.02
6	2720	6	?
7	3180	7	15.43
8	3630	8	17.64

_____

2   13   14   15   16   18

Circle the number which is divisible by
both 3 and 5.

3

What proportion of 3 hours is 10 minutes?

Circle the answer.

A $\frac{1}{3}$ **B** $\frac{1}{6}$ **C** $\frac{1}{18}$ **D** $\frac{1}{9}$ **E** $\frac{1}{12}$

4   DUD   FUF   EEE   POP   DOL

Which of these has a horizontal line of
symmetry? Circle the answer.

5–6

Where is
the court?

(____ , ____)

Where is the
fire station?

(____ , ____)

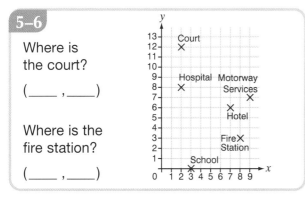

7

64 → $\div 8$ – $\times 5$ →

_____

Complete the function machine.

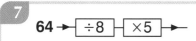

8

Edward has these coins in his pocket.
   1p 2p 5p 10p 10p 10p 10p £1

He selects a coin at random.

In which of the options below are both
statements true?

Circle the answer.

A He has an even chance of picking a
     10p coin out.
     He has an even chance of picking a
     coin less than 10p out.

B He has a less than even chance of
     picking a 2p coin out.
     He has a less than even chance of
     picking a 5p coin out.

C He has an even chance of picking a 1p
     coin out.
     He is certain to pick a coin of value £1
     or less.

D He has an even chance of picking a
     10p coin out.
     He has an even chance of picking a
     coin out greater than 10p.

E He is certain to pick a coin out that is
     less than £1.
     He has a less than even chance of
     picking a coin out that is less than 10p.

9   Which of these will hold about 10 litres?
Circle the answer.

A a teaspoon   **B** a cup

C a swimming pool   **D** a bucket

E a lake

10   What fraction is 10 mm of 30 cm?
Circle the answer.

A $\frac{1}{3}$ **B** $\frac{1}{30}$ **C** $\frac{10}{30}$ **D** $\frac{1}{300}$ **E** $\frac{1}{0.3}$

Total

1

A length of wire is d cm long.

It is cut to form an equilateral triangle of side x cm **and** a square of side y cm.

The perimeter of the equilateral triangle and the square are the same.

Read these statements.

Statement 1: $6x = d$

Statement 2: $8y = d$

Statement 3: $4x + 3y = d$

Circle the answer.

A All of the statements are correct.

B Only statement 3 is correct.

C Only statements 1 and 2 are correct.

2

Sam buys some apples which cost 27p each.

He pays for them with three one pound coins.

Kay buys the same number of bananas which cost 37p each.

She pays for them with four one pound coins.

They each receive the same amount of change.

How many pieces of fruit did each person buy?

_____

3

A canteen makes 456 pies.

They sell 322.

How many pies remain?

_____

4

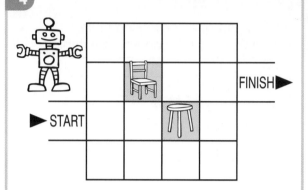

Guide the robot through the kitchen without hitting any hazards.

He can only move FORWARD, TURN LEFT 90° and TURN RIGHT 90°.

Circle the correct instructions.

A FORWARD 1, TURN RIGHT 90°, FORWARD 1, TURN RIGHT 90°, FORWARD 1

B FORWARD 2, TURN LEFT 90°, FORWARD 1, TURN RIGHT 90°, FORWARD 3

C FORWARD 2, TURN RIGHT 90°, FORWARD 1, TURN LEFT 90°, FORWARD 2, TURN LEFT 90°, FORWARD 2, TURN RIGHT 90°, FORWARD 1

D FORWARD 3, TURN RIGHT 90°, FORWARD 1, TURN LEFT 90°, FORWARD 2, TURN LEFT 90°, FORWARD 1, TURN RIGHT 90°, FORWARD 1

E FORWARD 3, TURN LEFT 90°, FORWARD 1, TURN LEFT 90°, FORWARD 2, TURN LEFT 90°, FORWARD 2, TURN RIGHT 90°, FORWARD 1

1 $\frac{1}{8}$ 60 minutes = 1 hour, so 2 × 60 = 120 minutes. 15 minutes out of 120 minutes is $\frac{15}{120}$. Simplify the fraction by dividing the numerator (top number) and denominator (bottom number) by the same number. The digits in the fraction are large, so do this in a couple of steps: 15 and 120 can both be divided by 5 and simplified to $\frac{3}{24}$; simplify again by dividing by 3 to get $\frac{1}{8}$.

2 **C** To change 24-hour clock into 12-hour clock, subtract 12 from the hours if they are between 13:00 and 23:59: 21 – 12 = 9, so it is 9.42. 00:00 to 11:59 is a.m. and 12:00 to 23:59 is p.m., so 21:42 is 9.42 p.m.

3 **B** First, add the missing numbers along the bottom (x-axis) and up the side (y-axis). Both have 10 increments between 0 and 1, so take the difference between these numbers (= 1) and divide it by the number of increments (1 ÷ 10 = 0.1). Then label each increment (e.g. 0.1, 0.2, 0.3, etc.). Write the increments on the grid, increasing by 0.1 each time: decimal numbers increase in the same way as whole numbers, so 0.1 is followed by 0.2, 0.3, 0.4 and so on. To write co-ordinates, use the phrase 'along the corridor and up the stairs'. This means along the x-axis then up the y-axis, so this number is second.

4–8 Refer to Question 3.

4 **(8.2, 8.5)** There are 10 increments between 8 and 9, so they will increase by 0.1 each time. The first number is 8 and will be followed by 8.1, 8.2, 8.3 and so on.

5 **(6, 7)**   6 **(5, 8)**
7 **A**   8 **C**

9–10 Whereas only one quadrant was shown in Question 3–8, four quadrants are shown here and −4 to 4 is also shown on each axis. Continue to use 'along the corridor and up the stairs' to write the co-ordinates in the correct order.

9 **E**

10 **(2, –2)** The sides of the square shown are 4 ones along and upwards: draw a line 4 squares downwards from B and a line 4 squares across from D to find (2, –2).

1 **A** Write the number in a place value grid to help write it in words.

10 000s	1000s	100s	10s	Ones
5	9	0	3	8

2–3 Use the place value grid shown in Question 1.

2 **90 909** Make sure zeros are included as 'place-holders'. For example, the number 909 needs a 0 otherwise it becomes 99, a completely different number.

3 **E** The 3 will be in the thousands column, so it is worth three thousand.

4 **A** Decimal numbers increase in the same way as whole numbers, for example, 2.3 is followed by 2.4, 2.5, 2.6 and so on; 2.38 is followed by 2.39, 2.40, 2.41 and so on. Only 2.40 is between 2.39 and 2.42.

5 **300** or **3 hundreds** The number has been multiplied by 10 each time. When a number is multiplied by 10, 100, 1000, etc, it is moved to the left on a place value grid: as 10 has one zero, it is moved 1 place each time (if multiplying by 100, it would be moved 2 places, as 100 has two zeros, and so on). Add a zero in the ones, tens, hundreds, etc, if they are left empty. 130 × 10 = 1 300 and 1 300 × 10 = 13 000. The 3 in the missing number is in the hundreds column.

100000s	10000s	1000s	100s	10s	ones
			1	3	0
		1	3	0	0
	1	3	0	0	0

6 **7.006** Place the numbers in a grid, ensuring the decimal points are aligned. Add a zero in any gaps after the decimal point, so all the numbers have the same amount of digits after it (7.6 is the same as 7.600, 7.06 is the same as 7.060, etc.). Look for the smallest number in the first column: if they are all the same, go onto the next column and so on.

7	•	6	0	0
7	•	0	6	0
7	•	6	0	0
7	•	0	0	6
7	•	6	0	0

7 $\frac{2}{3}$ 11 girls out of 30 pupils is $\frac{11}{30}$. When making approximations, numbers are rounded. In the fraction $\frac{11}{30}$, 30 is already rounded to the nearest 10 but $\frac{11}{30}$ needs to be rounded. To do this, identify the digit in the place value column you are rounding to and look at the digit that follows it: if it is 4 or less, just change it to zero; if it is 5 or more, change it to zero and increase the number in the column you are rounding to by 1. The 1 in the ones in 11 is rounded to 0 and the 1 in the tens column remains the same: 11

becomes 10 and the fraction is changed to $\frac{10}{30}$. This is the number of girls.

The whole class is $\frac{30}{30}$, so subtract $\frac{10}{30}$ from this to find the number of boys: $\frac{30}{30} - \frac{10}{30} = \frac{20}{30}$. When subtracting fractions, only subtract the numerators (top numbers) and leave the denominator (bottom numbers) the same. $\frac{20}{30}$ can be simplified to $\frac{2}{3}$ (refer to Test 1 Q 1 on simplifying fractions).

8 **$\frac{4}{5}$** Write the proportions as fractions: the whole amount is $\frac{2500}{2500}$ and the concentrate is $\frac{500}{2500}$. First, simplify the fractions (refer to Test 1 Q 1) by dividing by 100. When a number is divided by 10, 100, 1000, etc, it is moved to the right on a place value grid: as 100 has two zeros, move it 2 places (if it were 1000, it would move 3 places and so on). $2500 \div 100 = 25$ and $500 \div 100 = 5$, so the fractions become $\frac{25}{25}$ and $\frac{5}{25}$. Simplify further to get $\frac{5}{5}$ and $\frac{1}{5}$ then subtract: $\frac{5}{5} - \frac{1}{5} = \frac{4}{5}$ (refer to Q 7 on subtracting fractions).

1000s	100s	10s	ones	Decimal Point	10s	100s
2	5	0	0	•		
		2	5	•	0	0
	5	0	0	•		
			5	•	0	0

9–10 Refer to Question 7 on rounding.

9 **7.63** A number with 2 decimal places has two digits after the decimal point: 3 is followed by 2. As that is less than 4, the 3 remains the same and is rounded to 7.63.

10 **9.00** 9 is two places after the decimal and followed by 5, so the 9 needs to increase by 1. When the digit 9 is increased, it becomes 0 and the digit to its left is increased by 1. However, this digit is also 9, so the same thing happens again: 9 becomes a 0 and the digit to its left is increased by 1, so 8 becomes 9. As the number is being rounded to two decimal places, it still needs two digits after the decimal, even if they are zeros.

Test 3: Shape and Space (p 5)

1 **D** Look at the corner of each shape: the smallest gap shown on the interior of a corner is in the triangle.

2 **E** Diagonals are straight lines that go from corner to corner on a 2D shape.

3 **SIH** A full turn is 360°, so a half-turn is 180°. Turn the page upside down (a half-turn) to find the answer.

4 **D** If a shape looks exactly the same after it has been rotated, then it has rotational symmetry. Only option D is able to do this.

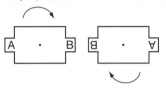

5 **LAL** Vertical lines of symmetry will be through the centre, running from top to bottom. A mirror image of the letters needs to be shown to the left and right of the line of symmetry.

6 **DID** Horizontal lines of symmetry will be through the centre, running from left to right. A mirror image of the letters needs to be shown above and below the line of symmetry.

--DID-- -CAT- -HUH- -NUN- -TAT-

7–8 **44, 32** First, find the missing lengths by separating the shape into rectangles:

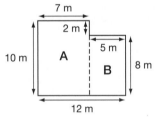

Use the measurements given on the opposite sides to calculate the missing ones. The perimeter of a shape is the total length around the outside: $10 + 7 + 2 + 5 + 8 + 12 = 44$.

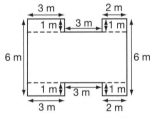

Find the missing dimensions using subtraction. The perimeter is $6 + 3 + 1 + 3 + 1 + 2 + 6 + 2 + 1 + 3 + 1 + 3 = 32$.

9 **D** Shapes A, B and E are all regular shapes, so each of their sides are the same length. A is $3 \times 4 = 12$; B is $4 \times 3 = 12$; E is $6 \times 2 = 12$. In shapes C and D, the opposite sides are the same length: $C = 2 + 2 + 4 + 4 = 12$; $D = 1 + 1 + 6 + 6 = 14$.

10 **A** All the sides are the same length and the missing length is represented with *a*. There are 12 sides and 12 × *a* is written as 12*a* in algebra because the 'x' sign is not used.

Test 4: Data Handling (pp6–7)

1 **40** One full bar represents 10 and 4 full bars shown for Wednesday. 4 × 10 = 40

2 **A** 39 were sold on Monday (6 × 6) + 3 = 39) and 27 were sold on Wednesday (4 × 6) + 3 = 27); 39 − 27 = 12.

3–4 Align a ruler with the top of the bars to see which numbers they are level with on the *y*-axis.

3 **5** 7 were bought on Tuesday and 12 on Friday. 12 − 7 = 5

4 **28** The bar for Maths is level with 30. The bar for Geography is just below half-way between 0 and 5 (2.5 or $2\frac{1}{2}$), so it represents 2 pupils: 30 − 2 = 28.

5 **7** 6 pupils completed 21–30 laps and 1 pupil completed 31–40 laps: 6 + 1 = 7.

6 **23** 20 pupils scored 20–29; 1 pupil scored 30–39; and 2 pupils scored 40–49: 20 + 1 + 2 = 23.

6–10 Probability is the chance of something happening out of a total number of possible outcomes. For example, on a dice, the number 5 has 1 chance out of 6 of being thrown as there is only 1 number 5 on a dice and a dice has 6 sides. This can be written as 1 in 6 or $\frac{1}{6}$. When comparing possible outcomes, it is best to write them as fractions on a number line. (Remember that $\frac{1}{2}$ is the same as an even chance and all possible outcomes always add up to 1).

7 **C** Find the total amount of marbles to find how many possible outcomes there are: 2 + 4 + 6 = 12 possible outcomes. As there are 12, mark the possibilities on a number line as twelfths: red is 2 out of 12 ($\frac{2}{12}$), green is 4 out 12 ($\frac{4}{12}$) and yellow is 6 out of 12 ($\frac{6}{12}$). As $\frac{6}{12}$ can be simplified to $\frac{1}{2}$, it is the same as an even chance.

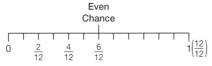

8 **B** There are 6 sides on a dice, so mark the possibilities on a number line as sixths: rolling an even number is $\frac{3}{6}$ as there are 3 even numbers; rolling a number less than six is $\frac{5}{6}$ as there are 5 numbers less than 6; rolling a prime number is $\frac{3}{6}$ as there are 3 prime numbers (2, 3 and 5) and so on. A prime number is a number that can only be divided by the number 1 and itself. For example, 7 is a prime number as it can only be divided by 1 and 7 (1 is not a prime number as it cannot be divided by 1 and another number).

9 $\frac{21}{23}$ 3 + 2 + 5 + 6 + 7 = 23 balls. Subtract the number of red balls to find the possibility of not picking one: 23 − 2 = 21, so the chance is $\frac{21}{23}$.

10 **0.75** or $\frac{3}{4}$ or **75%** There are 4 different numbers, so 4 possible outcomes. 3 of those numbers are greater than 1, so the chance is 3 out of 4 ($\frac{3}{4}$). Equivalent answers of 0.75 and 75% are also acceptable.

Test 5: Number (p8)

1–4 A square number is a number that is multiplied by itself. For example, 4² is 4 × 4 = 16, so 16 is a square number. A cubed number is a number that is multiplied by itself, then multiplied by itself again. For example, 2³ is the same as 2 × 2 × 2 = 8 so 8 is a cubed number. Write a list of square and cubed numbers up to 16 to help answer the questions. Refer to Test 4 Q 8 on prime numbers.

1 **15**   2 **1**

3 **A** Only option A shows two prime numbers: 3 + 5 = 8, which is 2³.

4 **4** Odd numbers are shown in an increasing order, so Line 6 would show: 1 + 3 + 5 + 7 + 9 + 11 = 36: 3, 5, 7 and 11 are prime numbers.

5–10 Use column addition and column subtraction. When using column addition, work from right to left and make sure any numbers carried over are added on in the next column. When using column subtraction, make sure the larger number is at the top. Work from right to left and make sure you exchange from the next column if the number above is bigger than the one below if the number above it is smaller. If calculating decimals, line them up so that they are in the same column and place a decimal in the answer space, aligned with the others, to make sure it is in the correct place in the answer. Add a 0 to any places that are left empty.

5 **283** Subtract the total number of people who preferred curries and stir-fries from 567: 78 + 206 = 284 and 567 − 284 = 283.

```
    2   0   6
+       7   8
    2   8   4
        1
   ⁴5  ¹6   7
−   2   8   4
    2   8   3
```

6 **6** Subtract the total amount of children acting and assisting backstage from 127: 72 + 49 = 121; 127 − 121 = 6.

7–8 258, 42 986 − 728 = 258. Find the new total of meals and subtract 986: 728 + 300 = 1028; 1028 − 986 = 42.

$$
\begin{array}{r}
{}^{0}\!4\;\;{}^{9}\!0\;\;{}^{1}\!2\;\;8\\
-\qquad 9\;\;8\;\;6\\
\hline
0\;\;4\;\;2
\end{array}
$$

9 21 Find the total of people that get on and the total that get off, then subtract to find how many are left: 35 + 14 + 12 + 6 = 67 get on, 2 + 16 + 28 = 46 get off; 67 − 46 = 21.

10 £53.63 Subtract £5.00 from £58.63.

$$
\begin{array}{r}
5\;\;8\;\bullet\;6\;\;3\\
-\qquad 5\;\bullet\;0\;\;0\\
\hline
5\;\;3\;\bullet\;6\;\;3
\end{array}
$$

Test 6: Data Handling (p 9)

The mode is the number that occurs the most often. To find the median, write the numbers in order from smallest to largest: the number in the middle is the median. To find the mean, add all the numbers together, then divide by the amount of numbers you have added. The range is the difference between the smallest and largest number.

1 27 27 occurs most often.

2 Purple Most pupils chose purple, so this is the modal colour.

3 D £110, £120, £130, £140, £150, £220, £435: £140 is in the middle.

4 40 000 Divide 960 000 by 24 to find the mean. Use short division to complete the sum. 24 does not go into 9, so write a zero above it and carry the 9 over to the next column to create the number 96. 24 goes into 96 four times, so write 4 above 96 (use repeated addition: 24 + 24 + 24 + 24 = 96 (4 lots of 24). 24 goes into zero 0 times, so write 0 above the remaining digits.

$$
\begin{array}{r}
0\;\;4\;\;0\;\;0\;\;0\;\;0\\
2\;\;4\;\overline{\smash{)}\,9\;\;{}^{9}\!0\;\;0\;\;0\;\;0\;\;0}\\
6
\end{array}
$$

5 E 199 − 174 = 25 (refer to Test 5 Q 5–10 on column subtraction).

6 A 8 − 0 = 8

7 C 13 − 1 = 12

8 B 5, 7, 12, 19, 20: 12 is in the middle.

9 12 The total number of cups has been divided by 5 days to get the answer of 7 (35 ÷ 5 = 7). The number of cups needs to add up to 35. Add the numbers shown for each day and subtract from 35 to find the answer: 35 − (2 + 8 + 9 + 4) = 35 − 23 = 12.

10 8 Refer to Question 9. Find the mean: 45 ÷ 5 = 9; find the missing number: 45 − (12 + 13 + 8 + 4) = 45 − 37 = 8.

Test 7: Shape and Space (pp 10–11)

1 D Copy and cut out the nets shown, then assemble each to find the answer.

2 D Use column multiplication to find 30 × 30 = 900. Then, multiply 900 by the number of squares in the shape using long multiplication: 25 × 900 = 22 500.

$$
\begin{array}{r}
9\;\;0\;\;0\\
\times\qquad 2\;\;5\\
\hline
4\;\;5\;\;0\;\;0\\
+\;\;1\;\;8\;\;0\;\;0\;\;0\\
\hline
2\;\;2\;\;5\;\;0\;\;0\\
1
\end{array}
$$

The answer is in m²: 100 cm = 1 metre, so 1 m² = 100 cm × 100 cm = 10 000 cm, so divide 22 500 by 10 000 to change it into m². 22 500 ÷ 10 000 = 2.25 (refer to Test 2 Q 5 on dividing by powers of 10).

3 35 To find the area of a parallelogram, use length × height: 7 × 5 = 35.

4 A Separate the shape into a rectangle and two triangles: the area of a rectangle is width × length; the area of a triangle base × height ÷ 2. In this question the y is a 'red herring' and not needed to calculate the answer.

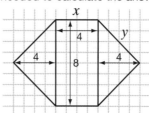

$x = 4$ squares. The length of the rectangle is 8, which is 2 lots of 4 (2 lots of x), and can be written as $2x$. Therefore, the area of the rectangle x times $2x$, which is $2x^2$ (x times $x = x^2$).

The height of each triangle is $4 = x$ (imagine the triangles turned on their side). The base of each triangle is 8, which is $2x$. Therefore, the area is x times $2x$ divided by 2: x times $2x = 2x^2$ and $2x^2 \div 2 = 1x^2$, which is written as x^2 (1 is not used with a letter in algebra).

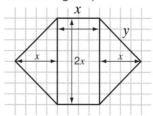

The total area of the shape is found by adding the measurements together, so: $2x^2$ (rectangle) + x^2 (first triangle) + x^2 (second triangle) = $4x^2$.

5 **4** Draw the smaller triangle inside the larger one, carefully measuring half-way along the side of the larger triangle.

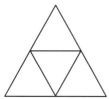

6 **D** Copy and cut out the nets shown, then assemble each to find the answer.

7–10 Refer to Question 4 on finding the area of a rectangle and triangle. The perimeter of a shape is the total length around the outside.

7 **24** $4 \times 12 \div 2 = 24$. Group the items to make the sum easier: 4×6 may be easier to calculate than $48 \div 2$.

8 **7.5** The base of the triangle is the same as the length of the rectangle and the height is the same as its width, so 15 just needs to be divided by 2 (refer to Test 6 Q 4 on short division).

9 **E** Find all the factors pairs of 70 to see which numbers could have been multiplied together to get an area of 70 cm². Factor pairs are two numbers that are multiplied together to make another number. 1 and 70, 2 and 35, 5 and 14, 7 and 10 are all factor pairs of 70. To find which pair has been used to calculate the area, add the numbers in each pair together and multiply by 2 (remember that a rectangle has 2 pairs of sides of equal length). Only $7 + 7 + 10 + 10$ gives one of the answers shown (34).

10 **C** Two sides are 10 cm, subtract this from 24 to give 4. If both widths = 4 cm, then one width = 2 cm and 10 cm × 2 cm = 20 cm².

Test 8: Number (p 12)

1–4 To compare fractions, decimals and percentages, convert all the options shown into decimals and write them in a decimal grid (as shown below in Question 1). To convert fractions into decimals, divide the numerator (top number) by the denominator (bottom number) using short division (refer to Test 6 Q 4). For example, $\frac{1}{2}$ is $1 \div 2 = 0.5$. To convert percentages into decimals, write the numbers in the percentage after the decimal point, e.g. 25% = 0.25.

1 **$\frac{4}{9}$** $\frac{1}{2} = 0.5$, $\frac{6}{10} = 0.6$, $\frac{3}{5} = 0.6$, $\frac{4}{9} = 0.444$ and $\frac{5}{8} = 0.625$. Align the decimals in a grid. Look for the smallest number in the first column: if they are all the same go onto the next column, and so on. 0.444 is the smallest here, the equivalent of $\frac{4}{9}$.

0	•	5	0	0
0	•	6	0	0
0	•	6	0	0
0	•	4	4	4
0	•	6	2	5

2 **$\frac{2}{5}$** $\frac{2}{5} = 0.4$, 20% = 0.20, $\frac{1}{3} = 0.33$, 35% = 0.35. Place in a grid, as shown in Question 1: 0.4 is the largest, the equivalent of $\frac{2}{5}$.

3–4 To find a fraction of the number, divide the number by the denominator (bottom number) in the fraction and multiply the answer by the numerator (top number). For example, $\frac{3}{4}$ of 200 is: $200 \div 4 = 50$ then $50 \times 3 = 150$, so $\frac{3}{4}$ of 200 = 150.

3 **D** Knowledge of common fraction, percentages and decimal equivalents is needed here. $\frac{3}{4}$, 75% and 0.75 are the same value, so options A, B and C will produce the same answer: all are 150. To calculate option D, '0.5 of' is equivalent to '$\frac{1}{2}$ times': $\frac{1}{2} \times 400 = 200$. To find 150% in option E, partition 150 into 100 and 50: 100% is the full amount (100 here); 50% is the equivalent of $\frac{1}{2}$, which is 50; $100 + 50 = 150$.

4 **D** Use knowledge of common fraction, percentages and decimal equivalents here. 62% is 0.62 so A is less than B. $\frac{3}{5} = 0.6$ or 60%, also less than B. $\frac{2}{3}$ is 0.67 or 67% (rounded) – now D is larger than B. For option E, $\frac{1}{8}$ is 0.125, $\frac{5}{8}$ is 5 × 0.125 = 0.625 or 62.5% so this is less than D.

5–7 To change a fraction into a percentage, find the equivalent fraction with a denominator of 100 by multiplying the numerator (top number) and denominator (bottom number) by the same number. The numerator is the percentage. For example, $\frac{1}{5}$ can be changed to $\frac{20}{100}$ by multiplying both numbers by 20 and $\frac{20}{100} = 20\%$.

5 **68%** 17 out of 25 is $\frac{17}{25}$: to find the percentage, $\frac{17}{25} \times 100$, simplify by dividing the 100 and 25 to give $17 \times 4 = 68\%$.

6 **40%** 6 out of 15 boxes are shaded $= \frac{6}{15}$ which can be simplified to $\frac{2}{5}$ (refer to Test 1 Q 1 on simplifying fractions). To find the percentage, $\frac{2}{5} \times 100 = 2 \times 20 = 40\%$.

7 **74%** $50 - 13 = 37$, so he has $\frac{37}{50}$ left: to find the percentage, simplify $\frac{37}{50} \times 100$ to give $37 \times 2 = 74\%$.

8 **80** Refer to Question 4 on finding the percentage of a number: $400 \times \frac{20}{100}$ and simplify to $4 \times 20 = 80$.

9 **£1200** $\frac{1}{3}$ of £1800 = £600; £1800 – £600 = £1200.

10 **280** The fraction is shown in tenths, so the whole 1400 is $\frac{10}{10}$ and $\frac{10}{10} - \frac{8}{10} = \frac{2}{10}$. Therefore, $\frac{2}{10}$ bought other brands (refer to Test 2 Q 7 on subtracting fractions). $\frac{2}{10}$ of 1400 = $\frac{2}{10} \times 1400 = 2 \times 140 = 280$.

Test 9: Shape and Space (p13)

1–2 To find the volume, multiply the length by the width by the height.

1 **250** 10 × 5 = 50 and 50 × 5 = 250

2 **0.5** 2 × 0.5 = 1 and 1 × 0.5 = 0.5

3 **6.26** Refer to Test 2 Q 4 on decimal numbers.

4–5 Refer to Test 5 Q 5–10 on column addition and subtraction.

4 **D** 1 kg is approximately the same weight as 1 litre: 2 litres × 3 = 6 litres; 6 litres + 1.5 litres + 1 kg = 8.5 kg (6.0 + 1.5 + 1.0 = 8.5).

5 **A** 1000 g = 1 kg, so convert 850 g into kg by dividing by 1000: 850 ÷ 1000 = 0.850 kg (refer to Test 2 Q 8 on dividing by powers of 10). 25.800 – 0.850 = 24.950 = 24.95

6 **E** Use knowledge of the height or length of items you are familiar with, e.g. the height of a door is approximately 2 metres, so a tall man is approximately 2 metres tall. 6 × 2 m = 12 m.

7 **C** Use knowledge of the weight of items you are familiar with, e.g. a large bottle of water is 1.5 litres, so 50 litres is the most appropriate measurement.

8 **B** Refer to Question 7.

9 **70** Separate the shape into two rectangles and add the missing measurements (refer to Test 3 Q 7–8). Find the area of each rectangle, by multiplying the length by the width, and add the answers together to find the total area. There are two options here: (8 × 5) + (6 × 5) = 70 or (2 × 5) + (6 × 10) = 70. One of these is easier than the other to calculate quickly.

10 **D** The large triangle is made up of 9 triangles the same size as the shaded one: 9 × 1000 = 9000 mm². However, this is not one of the options given in mm2, so convert this into cm². 10 mm = 1 cm, so 1cm² = 10 mm × 10 mm = 100 mm, so divide by 100 to convert it into cm²: 9000 ÷ 100 = 90.

Test 10: Number (p14)

1–5 Refer to Test 8 Q 3–4 on finding a fraction of a number and Test 2 Q 7 on subtracting fractions.

1 **16** (24 ÷ 3) × 2 = 16

2 **120** (300 ÷ 5) × 2 = 120

3 **175** The whole amount of 250 can be written as

$\frac{10}{10}$ and $\frac{10}{10} - \frac{3}{10} = \frac{7}{10}$. Therefore $\frac{7}{10}$ ordered white coffee. (250 ÷ 10) × 7 = 175

4 **40** The whole amount of 200 = $\frac{5}{5}$ and $\frac{5}{5} - \frac{4}{5} = \frac{1}{5}$. So, $\frac{1}{5}$ of flights are international and $\frac{1}{5}$ of 200 = 40.

5 **10** Add the fractions shown by adding the numerators (top numbers) and leaving the denominators the same: $\frac{1}{13} + \frac{7}{13} = \frac{8}{13}$; $\frac{13}{13}$ = the whole 26 miles, so he walked $\frac{13}{13} - \frac{8}{13} = \frac{5}{13}$. (26 ÷ 13) × 2 = 4

6 **46** minutes 115% means an increase of 15% on top of the original amount. 10% of 40 = 4 minutes and 5% = 2 minutes so 40 + 10 + 5 = 46 minutes.

7 **£32** Refer to Test 2 Q 7 on subtracting fractions and Test 8 Q 3 on finding a fraction of a number. As the fractions are eighths, the whole £64 = $\frac{8}{8}$; $\frac{8}{8} - \frac{1}{8} = \frac{7}{8}$ and $\frac{7}{8} - \frac{3}{8} = \frac{4}{8}$, so Nabeel receives $\frac{4}{8} = \frac{1}{2}$. 64 × $\frac{1}{2}$ = 32.

8 **£24** Refer to Test 8 Q 4 on finding a percentage of a number. £30 × 20 = 600 and 600 ÷ 100 = 6; £30 – £6 = £24.

9–10 Refer to Test 2 Q 5 on multiplying by powers of 10 and Test 1 Q 1 on simplifying fractions.

9 $\frac{1}{5}$ 1 litre = 1000 ml, so multiply 2.5 l by 1000 to change it into ml = 2500. Therefore, 500 out of 2500 is concentrate, $\frac{500}{2500} = \frac{1}{5}$ when simplified.

10 $\frac{1}{200}$ 1 kg = 1000 g, so multiply 4 kg by 1000 to change it into g = 4000. Therefore 20 out of 4000 is fat, which is $\frac{20}{4000} = \frac{1}{200}$ when simplified.

Test 11: Algebra (p15)

The multiplication sign (×) is not used in algebra: when letters and numbers are placed next to one another, without a +, – × or ÷ sign between them, they need to be multiplied. For example, $2x$ means 2 times x. Also, $1x$ is written as x as the 1 is not usually shown: so, $1y = y$, $1z = z$ and so on. Letters used to represent values can be added, subtracted, multiplied and divided in the same way as numbers: for example, $3a + 2a = 5a$; $6b \times 2 = 12b$; $21p \div 3p = 7p$, $q \times q = q^2$.

1 **16** Write the question as a missing number sentence: $\boxed{?} \times 4 + 12 = 76$. Work backwards through the equation completing the inverse (multiply instead of dividing, subtract instead of adding, etc): 76 – 12 = 64; 64 ÷ 4 = 16 (refer to Test 6 Q 4 on short division).

2 **3** The red marbles are represented by x; he has 3 more blue than red, which is $x + 3$; he has 4 times as many green as red, which is $4x$. This gives the equation $x + x + 3 + 4x = 21$ Add each

'x' together to simplify the equation to $6x + 3 = 21$, which is the same as $\boxed{?} + 3 = 21$. $18 + 3 = 21$, so $6x = 18$ and $x = 3$.

3　**6** As it is 3 consecutive numbers, divide 21 by 3 ($21 \div 3 = 7$). Add one and subtract one to the answer to find the consecutive numbers: $7 - 1 = 6$ and $7 + 1 = 8$, so the numbers are 6, 7 and 8.

4　**3** First, add the two amounts of money together: £3.60 + £4.80 = £8.40 (refer to Test 5 Q 5–10 on column addition). Then, divide by 2 to find how much each person has at the end: £8.40 ÷ 2 = £4.20 (refer to Test 6 Q 4 on short division). Subtract this amount from how much Mike originally had: £4.80 − £4.20 = £0.60 (refer to Test 5 Q 10 on column subtraction). £0.60 is the same as 60p which is 3 × 20p coins.

5　**17** $5x = 25$ and $3y = 9$: $25 + 9 = 34$, so $2z = 34$ and $z = 17$.

6　**D** Find the total number of years: $5 + 7 = 12$ years. Akshay's age 5 years ago $= x$, so $12 + x$ is the answer.

7　**D** This equation involves balancing the values (letters and numbers) on each side of the equals sign (=): whatever is done to one side, the same must be done to the other side. The aim is to get a letter on its own on one side of the equals sign and a number on its own on the other. Complete the inverse to balance the sum (refer to Question 1). The equation can be written as $y = \frac{4}{5}x$ (so option A is correct). Begin by getting rid of the fraction by multiplying by 5 on both sides: $y = \frac{4}{5}$ times x　so this becomes　$5y = 4$ times x　4 times x is the same as $4x$, so the equation is now $5y = 4x$ (so, option C is correct). Continue balancing by dividing both sides by dividing by 4 to find $\frac{5}{4}y = x$ (so, option B is correct; even if the values are on different sides of the equation sign, it is still the same sum). Return to the original equation and divide both sides by x to get $\frac{y}{x} = \frac{4}{5}$ (so, E is correct). D is the only incorrect option.

8　**6x** Draw and label the rectangle to help find the answer: $x + 2x + x + 2x = 6x$.

9　**2x + 7y** 2 minibuses $= 2x$ and 7 coaches $= 7y$. As the total is being asked for, the sum is addition: $2x + 7y$.

10　**3** Refer to Question 7 on balancing equations. Add 18 to both sides to get $7x + 9 = 10x - 0$ (if you add 9 you will have the sum $7x = 10x - 9$,

which will be harder to solve, so sometimes it is best to try both ways on each side and decide which gives the easier sum). $7x + 9 = 10x - 0$ is the same as $7x + 9 = 10x$. Then subtract $7x$ from each side to get $9 = 3x$, so $x = 3$.

When adding and subtracting positive and negative numbers, use a number line. Start at the number you are adding to or subtracting from: count to the right to add and to the left to subtract, for example, $-9 + 18 = 9$ and $-18 + 18 = 0$.

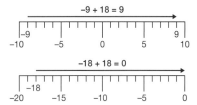

Test 12: Data Handling (pp 16–17)

1　**280** The whole pie chart represents 100%, so find the total percentage of the other cars and deduct the answer from 100%: 20% + 25% + 15% = 60% and 100% − 60% = 40%. 100% = 700 cars. Divide by 10 to find 10%: 700 ÷ 10 = 70, so 10% = 70 cars. 40% = 4 × 10% so multiply 70 × 4 to get 280.

2　**12.5 accept 12 or 13** The y-axis is shown as 2 squares going up in intervals of 8 km each time, so, one square is 4 km and 20 km will be half-way between 16 and 24. Use a ruler to draw a line across and mark where the diagonal crosses this line. The x-axis is shown as going up in intervals of 5 each time, so, one square is 2.5 miles. Draw a line down from the point marked on the diagonal: this will be half-way between 10 and 15 miles = 12.5 miles.

3　**22** Add all the numbers together and subtract the answer from 100: $17 + 29 + 13 + 7 + 12 = 78$ and $100 - 78 = 22$.

4　**A** Look at the box opposite to help decide. The missing option needs to be a question and have the answer of 'YES' if it is a chocolate sweet and 'NO' if it is a mint sweet, therefore 'Is it chocolate?' is the only option that works here.

5　**C** Mark the of co-ordinates on the graph and draw a line to join each pair (refer to Test 1 Q 3 on co-ordinates). Perpendicular lines are at right angles (90°) to one another, so, the answer is C.

6　**2** Add all the numbers together and subtract the answer from 100: $19 + 7 + 4 + 38 + 30 = 98$ and $100 - 98 = 2$.

7　**D** Refer to Test 4 Qs 6–10 on probability. $8 + 2 + 10 = 20$. Red $= \frac{8}{20}$, Green $= \frac{2}{20}$, Black $= \frac{10}{20}$.

8　**135** $12 \times 10 = 120$ and $3 \times 5 = 15$. $120 + 15 = 135$.

9 **16** Refer to Question 1. 15% + 20% + 40% = 75% and 100% − 75% = 25%. 25% of 64 is 16 (refer to Test 8 Q 4 on finding a percentage of a number). Or, $\frac{1}{4}$ of the pie chart shows children who preferred rowing and $\frac{1}{4}$ of 64 is 16 (refer to Test 8 Qs 3–4 on finding a fraction of a number).

10 **46** Find the total of the matches they won and drew: 7 + 8 + 13 + 2 + 6 + 10 = 46.

Test 13: Number (p18)

1 **624** Multiply 52 by 12 (refer to Test 7 Q 2 on long multiplication).

2 **13** Use long division to divide 312 by 24. Find how many times 24 goes into 31: only 1 24 goes into 31, so write 1 above and subtract 24 from 31 to find 7. Bring down the 2 from 312 to form the number 72 and use repeated addition to find how many times 24 goes into 72: 24 + 24 + 24 = 72, so write the 3 above.

```
          1   3
 2   4 | 3  1  2
    -   2  4
        0  7  2
    -      7  2
              0
```

3 **7** Use knowledge of the 3 times table to count up in 30s: 7 × 3 = 21, so 7 × 30 = 210. Therefore 7 complete pieces are made with 10 cm left over.

4 **53** Refer to Question 2 on long division: 2800 ÷ 53 = 52 remainder 44, so 53 coaches are needed.

5 **16** One row and column is added each time, so, the next pattern will show 4 × 4 = 16.

6 **D** A multiple is the result when two numbers are multiplied together: 5 × 7 = 35.

7 **D** Look at the sequence shown in each row: 1 is added each time to the grey tiles; 2 is added to the white tiles; and 3 is added to the total. Continue the sequence for each row: 3 + 1 = 4 grey tiles; 12 + 2 = 14 white tiles; and 15 + 3 = 18 tiles in total.

8 **20** List the factors of 4 and 5, then look for the lowest number in both lists (factors are numbers that can be divided into another number without leaving a remainder). Factors of 4 are 4, 8, 12, 16, 20 and factors of 5 are 5, 10, 15, 20. The answer is 20 as it is the first number to occur in both lists.

9 **24** As 12 is the larger number, use the 12 times table to count up: 1 × 12 = 12, which is not divisible by 8; 2 × 12 = 24, which is divisible by 8 (24 ÷ 8 = 3).

10 **39** Refer to Question 9: 3 × 13 = 39.

Test 14: Algebra (p19)

1 **3** $4a = 4 \times 5 = 20$; $2b = 2 \times 2 = 4$; $7c = 7 \times 3 = 21$. Rewrite the sum with the numbers: 20 + 4 − 21 = 3.

2 **E** Refer to Test 11 (including Qs 7 and 10 on balancing equations): in option A, both sides of the equation have been doubled; in option B, $3c$ has been subtracted from both sides of the equation; in option C, 20 has been subtracted from both sides; in option D, c has been added to each side. However, in option E, $2b$ has been subtracted from one side, but added to the other.

3 **83** Complete the inverse (refer Test 11 Q 1): 168 − 2 = 166; 166 ÷ 2 = 83.

4 **B** The rectangle's width = x, so its length = $x + 8$. The perimeter is the total length around the outside, so $x + x + (x + 8) + (x + 8) = 4x + 16$. One side of the square = y. As a square has 4 equal sides, the perimeter is $4y$. Subtract to find how much bigger it is: $4x + 16 − 4y$.

5 **1** Refer to Test 11 (including Q 7 and 10 on balancing equations): add $16x$ to both sides so the equation becomes $17 = 3 + 14x$ (write these values on a number line and calculate them in the same way as numbers: $−2x + 16x = 14x$). Then subtract 3 from both sides so it becomes $14 = 14x$; therefore, $x = 1$.

6 **96** 48 ÷ 3 = 16 (refer to Test 6 Q 4 on short division); 16 × 6 = 96.

7–9 Refer to Test 11 (including Q 7 and 10 on balancing equations).

7 **5** Subtract $2x$ from both sides so the equation becomes $x + 2 = 7$; then subtract 2 from both sides so it becomes $x = 5$.

8 **3** Add x to both sides so the equation becomes $32 = 23 + 3x$ ($−x + x = 0$); then subtract 23 from both sides so it becomes $9 = 3x$; therefore, $x = 3$.

9 **6** Write this as an equation to help solve it: she has x stamps and if she had 18 more, she would have 4 times as many ($4x$): $x + 18 = 4x$; subtract x from each side to get $18 = 3x$; so $x = 6$.

10 **14** Represent the son's age with a letter (x). The father is 36 years older, so his age can be written as ($x + 36$) and their total age can be written as (x) + ($x + 36$) = 64. Remove the brackets: $x + x + 36 = 64$, then simplify to $2x + 36 = 64$. Subtract 36 from both sides to find the value of $2x = 28$ therefore, $x = 14$.

Test 15: Shape and Space (pp20–21)

1–3 When counting along the squares, remember the one that you are 'standing on' does not need to be included.

1 **B**   2 **C**   3 **C**

4 B Draw along the diagrams to help find which one is possible: it is only possible on option B.

5 D A right angle is 90°.

6 E As the circle overlaps the triangle, the lines at the top of the triangle (inside the circle), and the bottom of the triangle are different streets. They form 'crossroads', and in real life, streets either side of a crossroads are separate, so these too can be considered as different streets.

7 B A reflex angle is greater than 180°.

8 150 Each corner of an equilateral triangle is 60° (angles in a triangle always add up to 180° so each angle will be 60° in an equilateral triangle). Each corner of a rectangle is 90° (angles in a quadrilateral always add up to 360°): 60° + 90° = 150°.

9 70 Refer to Question 8 on angles in a triangle: 180° − 80° − 30° = 70°.

10 D A right angle = 90° and angle b is larger, so it cannot be option B. 180° is a straight line and angle b is not larger than an angle on a straight line, so it cannot be A, C or E. Therefore, option D is the closest estimate.

Test 16: Mixed (p 22)

1 D In option D, the 2 outside the brackets multiplies everything inside the brackets: 2 times $2x = 4x$ and 2 times $y = 2y$, so $2(2x + y)$ can be simplified to $4x + 2y$.

2 B Refer to Test 4 Q 8 on prime numbers and Test 5 Qs 1–4 on square numbers. Only option B shows prime numbers and 17 + 19 = 36, which is 6².

3 18 Refer to Test 13 Q 2 on long division: 435 ÷ 23 = 18 remainder 21.

4 3 Refer to Test 11 (including Q 7 and 10 on balancing equations). Add x to both sides so the equation becomes $7x + 7 = 28$ ($−x + x = 0$); then subtract 7 from both sides so it becomes $7x = 21$; so, $x = 3$.

5 272 1 hour = 60 minutes and 4 × 60 is 240; 240 + 32 = 272.

6 C Use knowledge of the height or length of items you are familiar with, e.g. the height of a door is about 2 metres, so, a man's stride will be approximately 1 metre = 100 cm = 1000 mm. He takes 15 strides, so approximately 1500 cm (100 × 15 = 1500 – refer to Test 2 Q 5 on multiplying by powers of 10). The closest measurement to this is 1400 cm.

7 B 5 ham rolls = $5x$ and 3 tuna salads = $3y$. As the total is being asked for, the sum is addition: $5x + 3y$.

8 Fourteen thousand, two hundred and five Refer to Test 2 Q 1.

9 4.32 Refer to Test 2 Qs 7 and 10.

10 14 Refer to Test 6 Qs 1–4: 7, 9, 14, 21, 22.

Test 17: Mixed (p 23)

1 13.23 Find the difference between two numbers in the column with the missing value, then add the answer to 11.02: 17.64 − 15.43 = 2.21 and 11.02 + 2.21 = 13.23 (refer to Test 5 Qs 5–10 on column addition and subtraction).

2 15 Multiply the numbers together to find the answer: 5 × 3 = 15. If 15 is the product of 3 × 5, then it can be divided by 3 and 5 as well.

3 C 1 hour = 60 mins and 60 mins × 3 = 180 mins: 10 mins out of 180 is $\frac{10}{180}$ can be simplified to $\frac{1}{18}$ (refer to Test 1 Q 1 on simplifying fractions).

4 EEE Refer to Test 3 Q 6 on horizontal symmetry.

5–6 (2, 12), (8, 3) Refer to Test 1 Q 3 on co-ordinates.

7 40 Use times tables knowledge: 8 × 8 = 64, so 64 ÷ 8 = 8; 8 × 5 = 40.

8 B Refer to Test 4 Qs 6–10 on probability.

9 D Use knowledge of the volume of items you are familiar with, e.g. a large bottle of water is 1.5 litres, so a bucket is the most appropriate answer.

10 B 10 mm = 1 cm and 1 cm out of 30 cm is $\frac{1}{30}$.

Test 18: Mixed (pp 24–25)

1 C An equilateral triangle has 3 sides of equal length (in this case x) and a square has 4 sides of equal length (in this case y). The question can be written as the length of the wire, $d = 3x + 4y$. It is also true that the perimeters of the two shapes are the same so $3x = 4y$. Substituting this into the first equation, $d = 3x + 3x = 6x$; also $d = 4y + 4y = 8y$. Therefore, statements 1 and 2 are correct. $4x + 3y = d$ is incorrect.

2 10 List all the multiples of 27 and 37 (refer to Test 13 Q 6 on multiples). Sam pays with £3.00 and Kay pays with £4.00, so look for multiples in each list that have the last two digits the same: these amounts will give the same amount of change. 270 and 370 both end in 70, so, they both received 30p change. 27 × 10 = 270 and 37 × 10 = 370, so they each bought 10.

3 134 456 − 322 = 134 (refer to Test 5 Qs 7–8 on column subtraction).

4 C Refer to Test 15 Qs 1–3 on completing questions like this.

5 **C** Refer to Test 17 Q 1: 26.25 − 22.97 = 3.28 and 3.28 + 16.40 = 19.68.

6 **22** Refer to Test 12 Q 1. 30% + 15% + 15% = 60% and 100% − 60% = 40%. 100% = 55 households, so divide by 100 to find 1%: 55 ÷ 100 = 0.55 (refer to Test 2 Q 8 on dividing by powers of 10). Multiply the answer by 40 to find 40%: 0.55 × 40 = 22.00. To multiply a decimal number, remove the decimal point and multiply as normal (refer to Test 7 Q 2 on long multiplication): 40 × 55 = 2200. Then count the number of decimal places in the original sum: 40 × 0.55 has 2 digits after the decimal, so, there will be two digits after the decimal in the answer, so 2200 becomes 22.00 = 22.

7 **28** The perimeter of a shape is the total length around the outside: 6 + 9 + 3 + 5 + 5 = 28.

8 **D** Refer to Test 12 Q 2 on using conversion graphs. Find the difference between 130 and 100 on the axis that shows Fahrenheit (F°) = 30. If 3 squares = 30°, then 1 square = 10°. For the axis showing Celsius, find the difference between 0 and 10 = 10. If 2 squares = 10°, then 1 square = 5°.

9 **65** Refer to Test 13 Q 2 on long division: £1300 ÷ 20 = 65.

10 **A** Refer to Test 13 Q 6 on multiples. List all of the multiples of 3 and 5 up to 20 (the highest number shown) to find the answer. Use your knowledge of prime numbers: B and C both contain prime numbers cannot be multiples of 3 or 5.

Test 19: Mixed (p 26)

1 **0.4** When probability is written using decimals, the total of all the possible chances is 1.0, so 0.4 + 0.2 = 0.6 and 1.0 − 0.6 = 0.4.

2 **E** 1 m = 100 cm, so 6 m = 600 cm and 600 + 18 = 618 cm; 618 ÷ 3 = 206.

3 **NOS** Refer to Test 3 Q 4: NOS makes the word SON.

4 $\frac{1}{4}$ 1 hour = 60 mins and 3 × 60 = 180 mins. 45 mins out of 180 mins is $\frac{45}{180}$, which can be simplified to $\frac{1}{4}$ (refer to Test 1 Q 1 on simplifying fractions).

5 **486** 68 MB + 96 MB = 164 MB and 650 MB − 164 MB = 486 MB (refer to Test 5 Q 5–10 on column addition and subtraction).

6 **E** Draw the reflection onto the diagram using a ruler and protractor.

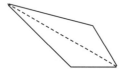

7 **5** Refer to Test 11 (including Questions 7 and 10 on balancing equations): add 2 to each side of the equation so it becomes $4x = 2x + 10$; then subtract $2x$ from each side so it becomes $2x = 10$, so, $x = 5$.

8 **E** 1 litre is approximately the equivalent to 1 kg = 1000 g and 500 g = 0.500 kg = 0.5 kg. 0.500. 1.5 + 1.5 + 3.0 + 0.5 = 6.5 kg

9 **221** 17 × 13 = 221 (refer to Test 7 Q 2 on long multiplication).

10 **29** Refer to Test 11 Q 1: 94 −7 = 87 and 87 ÷ 3 = 29.

Test 20: Mixed (p 27)

1 $\frac{7}{32}$ Refer to Test 8 Qs 1–4 on converting fractions into decimals to find the smallest: $\frac{1}{4}$ = 0.25, $\frac{3}{8}$ = 0.375, $\frac{2}{5}$ = 0.4, $\frac{2}{7}$ = 0.286 (rounded) and $\frac{7}{32}$ = 0.219 (rounded); therefore $\frac{7}{32}$ is the smallest.

2 **2z** $3x$ and $9y$ can be factorised to $3(x + 3y) = 6z$. Divide both sides by 3 to get $x + 3y = 2z$.

3 **J** Copy and cut out the net and assemble it to help find the answer.

4 **B** An obtuse angle is more than 90°, but less than 180°: only B does not have any as it has four right angles (90°).

5 **64** In a ratio, it is important to keep the calculations in the same order: girls to boys = 8 : 9 and the ratio has been changed to ? : 72. Find how many times 9 has been multiplied by to change it into 72 and multiply the girls by the same number: 9 × 8 = 72 and 8 × 8 = 64.

6 **E** 1 metre = 100 cm, so 2 m = 200 cm; 1 foot is approximately 30 cm. Find how many lots of 30 go into 200. Use knowledge of the 3 times table: if 3 × 6 = 18, then 30 × 6 = 180, so he is 6 feet. Convert the 20 cm remaining (200 − 180 = 20): one inch = 2.5 cm and 8 × 2.5 = 20, so 20 cm = 8 inches. Therefore he is 6 feet 8 inches and option E is closest to this measurement.

7 **P(−2, −3) Q(−3, 2) R(2, −3)** Refer to Test 1 Q 3 on co-ordinates.

8 **£60** Refer to Test 8 Qs 3–4 on finding a fraction of a number: $\frac{7}{7}$ = the whole £420 and $\frac{7}{7} - \frac{6}{7} = \frac{1}{7}$; £420 ÷ 7 = £60.

9 **4** $2y = 14$ and $z = 2$, so the equation can be rewritten as $4x − 14 = 2$. Complete the inverse to solve the sum (refer to Test 11 Q 1): $4x = 2 + 14$, so $4x = 16$ and therefore $x = 4$.

10 **132** Use knowledge of times tables: 11 × 11 = 121, so 121 ÷ 11 = 11; 11 × 12 = 132.

1 **C** The perimeter of a shape is the total length around the outside. Shapes A, B, C and D are all regular shapes, so each of their sides are the same length. A is 10 × 4 = 40; B is 8 × 5 = 40; C is 6 × 6 = 36; and D is 5 × 8 = 40. The opposite sides on the rectangle are the same, so 8 + 8 + 12 + 12 = 40.

2 **C** Draw the reflection onto the diagram using a ruler. An isosceles triangle has 2 sides and 2 angles of the same size.

3 **510** 620 + 200 + 200 = 1020 and 1020 ÷ 2 = 510.

4 **B** 1 foot = approximately 30 cm and 30 × 6 = 180 cm; as 100 cm = 1 m, divide 180 by 100 to find 1.8 m (refer to Test 2 Q 8 on dividing by powers of 10).

5 **34 (accept 33)** Refer to Test 12 Q 2 on using conversion graphs. There are 10 increments between 20° and 30°, so, each square along the x-axis represents 1°; the number of ice creams sold increases in increments of 5 every 2 squares, so each square represents 2.5 ice creams.

6 **D** Complete the drawing of the shape on the diagram: the shape has 10 sides of equal length, so it is a regular decagon.

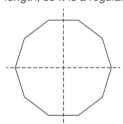

7 **C** Copy and cut out the net shown, then assemble it to find the answer.

8 **30** Separate the shape into 2 triangles and 1 rectangle, then work out the area of each shape (refer to Test 7 Q 4 on finding the area of a rectangle and triangle): 3 × 5 = 15; 15 ÷ 2 = 7.5 (refer to Test 1 Q 3 on short division). Add the answers together to find the total area: 7.5 + 15 + 7.5 = 30

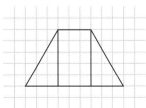

9 **45** The most popular subject is shown by the highest bar: English with 45.

10 **7** £3899 – £700 – £3199; use repeated addition to find how many lots of £457 make 3199 (short and long division will not work easily with this sum): 457 + 457 + 457 + 457 + 457 + 457 + 457 = 3199, i.e., 7 lots of £457 (see Test 5 Qs 5–10 on column addition and subtraction).

1 **B** Use the place value grid shown in Test 2 Q 1.

2 $\frac{2}{3}$ 40 out of 60 minutes is $\frac{40}{60}$ which can be simplified to $\frac{2}{3}$ (refer to Test 1 Q 1 on simplifying fractions).

3 **A** Refer to Test 5 Qs 1–4 on square and cubed numbers: 4^2 = 4 × 4 as the '2' represents the number 4 being multiplied twice; 2^3 = 2 × 2 × 2 as the '3' represents the number 2 being multiplied three times. Here 5 is multiplied six times, so the answer is 5^6.

4 **14** Each triangle is the same height and width of each square shown with the dashed lines, so separate each square into triangles as well: a total of 14 triangles are shown.

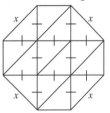

5 **£6.40** Each day: (12 × 4p) + (4 × 20p) = 128p. 128p × 5 days = 640p = £6.40.

6 **HIH** Refer to Test 3 Q 6 on horizontal symmetry.

7 **C** 25p coins do not exist, whereas all the other options show coins that do.

8 **C** The area of a square is found by multiplying the length by the width: as squares have sides of equal length, the length and the width are the same and 8 × 8 = 64. The perimeter is the total length around the outside and 8 × 4 sides = 32.

9 **0.98** Refer to Test 4 Qs 6–10 on probability. As the probability is shown in decimals, subtract 0.02 from 1 using column subtraction (refer to Test 5 Qs 5–10): 1.00 – 0.02 = 0.98.

10 **124** Refer to Test 3 Qs 7–8 on breaking down compound shapes and working out missing measurements: 8 × 6 = 48, 4 × 5 = 20, 7 × 8 = 56. Sum these 48 + 20 + 56 = 124. Or 6 × 4 = 24, 18 × 4 = 72, 4 × 7 = 28 gives 24 + 72 + 28 = 124.

Test 23: Mixed (p 31)

1 **600** Use the place value grid shown in Test 2 Q 1.

2 **£19.14** Refer to Test 7 Q 2 on long multiplication: 45p × 34 = 1530p; 32p × 12 = 384p; and 1530 + 384 = 1914p. As 100p = £1.00, divide by 100 (refer to Test 2 Q 8 on dividing by powers of 10): 1914 ÷ 100 = 19.14.

3 **E** A rectangle has two widths of equal length and two sides of equal length, so the total of the lengths is 40 (20 + 20); subtract this from 50 to find the total of both widths: 50 − 40 = 10, so each width is 5 (10 ÷ 2 = 5). Multiply the length by the width to find the area: 5 × 20 = 100.

4 **E** Ratio can be simplified or enlarged by dividing or multiplying both sides by the same number, so, equivalents of 14 : 20 are: 7 : 10 (when divided by 2); 28 : 40 (when multiplied by 2); 2 : $\frac{20}{7}$ (when divided by 7 – remember that $\frac{20}{7}$ is the same as 20 ÷ 7); which can be simplified further to 1 : $\frac{10}{7}$. Therefore E is the only option that has a different equivalent answer.

5 **C** Refer to Test 15 Q 8 on angles of an equilateral triangle and a quadrilateral: these are both less than 135°, so B and D can be excluded. To find the interior angle of a polygon, first, count the number of sides and subtract 2, then multiply the answer by 180°. Option C has 8 sides: 8 − 2 = 6; 6 × 180° = 1080. Divide the answer by the number of sides to find the size of each interior angle: 1080 ÷ 8 = 135.

6 **16:16** 13:47 + 2 hours = 15:47. As there are 60 minutes in an hour, subtract 47 from 60 to find the amount of minutes until the next hour (16:00): 60 − 47 = 13, then subtract 13 from the 29 minutes to find the amount of remaining minutes that need to be added: 29 − 13 = 16, so the time is 16:16.

7 **C** Count up in lots of 24 as this is the larger number: 2 × 24 = 48 and 4 × 12 = 48.

8 **120** Angles in a quadrilateral always add up to 360° and 90° is often represented with a small square, so: 60 + 90 + 90 = 240; 360 − 240 = 120.

9 **£42.30** Refer to Test 5 Qs 5–10 on column subtraction: 1.64 + 2.12 + 0.89 + 0.20 + 3.45 = 8.30 and 8.30 + 34.00 = 42.30.

10 $\frac{1}{6}$ Refer to Test 8 Qs 1–4 on converting fractions into decimals: $\frac{2}{3}$ = 0.667 (rounded); $\frac{4}{10}$ = 0.40; $\frac{5}{8}$ = 0.625; $\frac{1}{6}$ = 0.167 (rounded); $\frac{7}{10}$ = 0.70.

Test 24: Mixed (pp 32–33)

1 $\frac{5}{7}$ Refer to Test 8 Qs 1–4 on converting fractions and percentages into decimals: $\frac{5}{7}$ = 0.714; 71% = 0.71; 0.69; $\frac{2}{3}$ = 0.667 (rounded); 65% = 0.65.

2 **37.18** Refer to Test 2 Q 4 on decimals. The number line has 5 increments and the difference between 37.1 and 37. 2 is 0.1, so divide 0.1 by 5 to find how much it goes up by each time: 0.1 ÷ 5 = 0.02. Complete the number line by adding 0.02 to 37.1 onwards: 37.1 + 0.02 = 37.12, 37.12 + 0.02 = 37.14 and so on (refer to Test 5 Qs 5–10 on column addition).

3 **42** The two small lines on either side of the triangle and the word 'isosceles' indicate that those sides (and therefore angles) are the same. All angles in a triangle add up to 180°. 180 − 96 = 84, the total of the two remaining angles; 84 ÷ 2 = 42.

4 **42** Refer to Test 9 Qs 1–2 on volume: 7 × 3 = 21 and 21 × 2 = 42.

5 **16** The ratio is 1 cm : 2 km and 1 cm has been multiplied by 8, so 2 km needs to be multiplied by 8 as well (2 × 8 = 16).

6 **Mr Save** The amounts of money that are owed by people are shown with a '−' sign in front of them: the greatest amount owed shown is £468.

7 **360** To find the area of a triangle, multiply the base by the height and divide by 2: 18 × 40 = 720 and 720 ÷ 2 = 360.

8 **B** Refer to Test 15 Qs 1–3 on completing questions like this.

9 **E** Parallel lines are lines which are always the same distance apart; they never meet or cross. Vertical lines go from top to bottom and horizontal lines go from left to right.

10 **£70** Refer to Test 12 Q 2 on using conversion graphs.

Test 25: Mixed (p 34)

1 **0.04** Refer to Test 2 Q 4 on decimals: 0.04 is the same as 0.040.

2 **74** Refer to Test 11 Q 10 on calculating with negative numbers: 0 − 150 = −150 and −150 + 76 = −74; 0 m is sea level, so −74 is 74 m below sea level.

3 **NOOS** Refer to Test 3 Q 3. NOOS makes the word SOON.

4 **E** Refer to Test 8 Qs 1–4 on fractions, decimals and percentages. 0.1, 10% and $\frac{1}{10}$ are all the same amount, so, all give an answer of 2; 10% of 10 is 1, so 20% is 2; 0.01 is the same as 1% and 1% of 20 = 0.2. Also, percentages are

reversible and this can help to make the sum easier: 80% of 5 = 50% of 8 and one of these is easier to calculate than the other.

5 **5** Refer to Test 12 Q 2 on using conversions graphs.

6 **45** Write the question as a missing number sentence: $\boxed{?} \times 2 - 1 = 89$. Work backwards through the equation completing the inverse (refer to Test 11 Q 1). 89 + 1 = 90 and 90 ÷ 2 = 45.

7 **1000** Volume = length × width × height. All of these are the same for a cube, so 10 × 10 × 10 = 1000.

8 **B and C** Only a square and rhombus have diagonals that cross at right angles as they are both quadrilaterals with all sides the same length.

9 **102** As 6 is the larger number, use knowledge of times tables to find the first multiple of 6 after 100: 6 × 10 = 60 and 6 × 5 = 30; so 6 × 15 = 90; 90 + 6 = 96 and 96 + 6 = 102. Any number divisible by 6 will be divisible by 3.

10 **60** Jake is travelling in a ratio of 64 : 40, Lee is travelling in a ratio of 32 : 20 and both ratios can be simplified to 16 : 10 and then 8 : 5. Now divide 96 by 8 (using times table knowledge) = 12. The other side of his ratio can be found by multiplying 12 × 5 = 60.

Test 26: Mixed (p35)

1 **3.2** There are 10 increments between 0 and 2 so each increment is 2 ÷ 10 = 0.2. Complete the number line to find the answer by repeatedly adding 0.2 between 2 and 4: 2.2, 2.4, 2.6 and so on (refer to Test 2 Q 4 on decimals).

2 **180** 72 ÷ 6 = 12 and 12 × 15 = 180. Use long multiplication. Or split into (12 × 10) + (12 × 5) using times table knowledge.

3 **A** Use knowledge of the weight of items you are familiar with, e.g. a mug holds about 250 ml, so, a teaspoon is the most appropriate answer.

4 **D** Refer to Test 7 Q 9 on using factor pairs to find the answer. Factor pairs of 30 are: 1 and 30; 2 and 15; 3 and 10; and 5 and 6. Only 5 + 5 + 6 + 6 gives one of the answers shown (22).

5 **11** Refer to the first diagram on Test 11 Q 10 and use this to count up on: −2 to 9 is 11.

6 **5.99** Refer to Test 2 Qs 7 and 9.

7 **£2793** Round £3.99 to £4.00 to make the sum easier. If 7 × £4 = £28, then 700 × £4 = £2800. 700 lots of 1p were added when rounding, so subtract this from 2800: 700p = £7 and £2800 − £7 = £2793.

8 **6** A positive number is any number greater than zero. Write the question as a missing number sentence: $\boxed{?} \times \boxed{?} \div 2 = 18$. Work backwards through the equation, completing the inverse (refer to Test 11 Q 1). 18 × 2 = 36 and 6 × 6 = 36.

9 **D** Look at the box opposite to help decide. The missing option needs to be a question and have the answer of 'YES' if it is steel and 'NO' if it is paper, so, 'Is it strong?' is the only option that works.

10 $\frac{6}{7}$ $\frac{30}{35}$ can be simplified to $\frac{6}{7}$ (refer to Test 1 Q 1).

Test 27: Mixed (pp36–37)

1 **E** The ratio shown is 1 : 25 000, which means 1 cm = 25 000 cm in real life. 1 cm has been multiplied by 4, so 25 000 needs to be multiplied by 4 as well: if 4 × 25 = 100, then 4 × 25 000 = 100 000. Therefore the ratio becomes 4 : 100 000 and 100 000 cm is the equivalent of 1 km (there are 100 cm in 1 m and 1000 m in 1 km: 100 × 1000 = 100 000 cm).

2 **E** Refer to Test 24 Q 9. Perpendicular lines are at right angles (90°) to one another.

3 **D** Begin by changing 8.27 pm into 24-hour clock by adding 12 to the hours: 8 + 12 = 20, so 8.27 pm is 20:27. Remember that the 24-hour finishes the day at 23:59, then begins the next day at 00:00. Use a number line to count on 6 hours.

6 hours

20:27   21:27   22:27   23:27   00:30   01:27   02:27

4 **D** Refer to Test 15 Qs 1–3 on completing questions like this.

5 **3.5** If 1000 mA = 1 amp, then 500 mA = 0.5 amp and 4000 mA = 4 amps. The current drops by 500 mA, so 4 amps − 0.5 amp = 3.5 amps.

6 **B** Change the number of hours shown to minutes: there are 60 minutes in 1 hour, so 2 hours = 120 minutes and 3 hours = 180 minutes. Write these calculations as the denominator (bottom number) and the number of minutes shown as the numerator (top number). A = $\frac{30}{120}$, B = $\frac{20}{180}$, C = $\frac{15}{120}$, D = $\frac{40}{60}$ and E = $\frac{10}{60}$. Next, convert the fractions so they have the same denominator. 180 is the largest denominator, so count up in lots of 180: 180 × 2 = 360; 120 and 60 also go into 360. Remember to multiply the numerator and denominator by the same number: e.g. 120 × 3 = 360, so the numerators need to be multiplied by 3 as well. A = $\frac{90}{360}$, B = $\frac{40}{360}$, C = $\frac{45}{360}$, D = $\frac{240}{360}$ and E = $\frac{60}{360}$.

7 **B** The top two corners are right angles, as the arrows indicate parallel lines, so, they are 90° each. Angle c is obtuse (more than 90°, but less than 180°), so the answer must be option A or B. The size of the angle is slightly larger than 90°, so B is the most appropriate answer.

8 **16** $12 \times 8 = 96$: this means 96 grooves on the first cog have rotated, so find how many lots of 6 are in 96 to find how many revolutions the smaller cog makes; $96 \div 6 = 16$.

9 **63** $27 \times 7 = 189$ and $189 \div 3 = 63$.

10 **2** 50% is equivalent to $\frac{1}{2}$ (refer to Test 1 Q 1). The shape has been separated into sixths and $\frac{1}{6}$ is already shaded: 2 more triangles need to be shaded to make $\frac{1}{2}$ (50%).

Test 28: Mixed (p38)

1 **26** Add all the numbers together and subtract the total from 100: $3 + 12 + 23 + 18 + 18 = 74$ and $100 - 74 = 26$.

2 **12** A positive number is any number to the right of the zero on a number line (refer to the first diagram shown in Test 11 Q 10). Use knowledge of times tables: $12 \times 12 = 144$.

3 **£350000** Divide 14000 by 1000 to simplify the sum: $14 \times 25 = 350$. Then multiply the answer by 1000 to return it to its original form: $350 \times 1000 = 350000$ (see Test 7 Q 2 on long multiplication and Test 2 Qs 5 and 8 on multiplying and dividing by powers of 10).

4 **135** The difference between each adjacent number is 13 and each row and column has the following numbers: 109, 135 and 148.

5 **63%** Refer to Test 1 Q 1 on simplifying fractions and Test 8 Qs 5–7 on converting fractions into percentages: As a percentage, 378 out of 600 is $\frac{378}{600} \times 100 = \frac{378}{6}$. Use short division to find 63%.

6 **11** Add all the numbers together and subtract the total from 100: $13 + 1 + 18 + 54 + 3 = 89$ and $100 - 89 = 11$.

7 **0.036** Refer to Test 9 Qs 1–2 on volume and Test 18 Q 6 on multiplying decimals: $2 \times 6 \times 3 = 36$. There are 3 decimal places in the sum $0.2 \times 0.6 \times 0.3$, so there will be 3 decimal places in the answer, so it becomes 0.036.

8 **C** An edge is where two faces meet and shape D has 12 edges: $12 - 3 = 9$ and only option C has 9 edges.

9 **195** Find 10% by dividing by 10, then multiply the answer by 3 to find 30%: $150 \div 10 = 15$ and $15 \times 3 = 45$. Add 45 to 150 g to find the answer: $45 + 150 = 195$.

10 **4p** Refer to Test 11 (including Qs 7 and 10 on balancing equations). The equation is $p = \frac{3}{4}q$ ($\frac{3}{4}$ of q is the same as 3 ÷ 4 times q). Multiply both sides of the equation by 4 to change it to $4p = 3q$.

Test 29: Mixed (p39)

1 **50000** Refer to the diagrams on Test 11 Q 10 on negative numbers. As negative numbers 'mirror' positive numbers, −67 is the lowest temperature shown, therefore the coldest.

2 **B** Refer to Test 24 Q 3: $47 + 47 = 94$ and $180 - 94 = 86$.

3 **$\frac{4}{5}$** 40 out of 50 is $\frac{40}{50}$ and can be simplified to $\frac{4}{5}$ (refer to Test 1 Q 1).

4 **B** Refer to Test 6 on range: $197 - 171 = 26$.

5 **50x + 20y** The boxes of pencils = 50x and the boxes of pens = 20y. The question is asking how many she orders altogether, so the sum is addition: $50x + 20y$.

6 **6.63** Refer to Test 2 Q 4 on decimals. The number line has 5 increments between 6.55 and 6.65, so divide (6.65×6.55) by 5 to find the value of each increment (= 0.02) (refer to Test 1 Q 3 on short division). Complete the number line by adding 0.02 to 6.55 onwards: $6.55 + 0.02 = 6.57$, $6.57 + 0.02 = 6.59$ and so on (refer to Test 5 Qs 5–10 on column addition).

7 **16** Refer to Test 13 Q 2 on long division: $293 \div 18 = 16$ remainder 5, so 16 complete packets.

8 **D** Both sides of the ratio need to be divided by or multiplied by the same number to find an equivalent ratio: only 5 : 1 cannot do this.

9 **15** Refer to Test 5 Qs 1–4 on square and cubed numbers.

10 **116 or 117** Subtract to find the answer: $1453 - 1337 = 116$, but the year the war began needs to be included too, so 116 + 1 year = 117. However, either answer is acceptable.

Test 30: Mixed (pp40–41)

1 **y + 15** Find the total number of years: $13 + 2 = 15$ years. Stu's age 13 years ago = y, so y + 15 is the answer.

2 **Thursday** The least amount of loaves were sold on Thursday (5 rolls).

3 **144** Refer to Test 8 Qs 3–4 on finding a fraction of a number: $360 \div 5 = 72$, so $\frac{1}{5} = 72$ and $\frac{2}{5} = 144$. $360 - 72 = 288$ and $288 - 144 = 144$ (refer to Test 5 Qs 5–10 on column subtraction).

4 **A** Refer to Test 1 Q 3 on co-ordinates.

5 **210** Refer to Test 12 Q 1.14% + 12% + 46% = 72%, and 100% − 72% = 28%. 100% =

750 people, so divide by 100 to find 1%: 750 ÷ 100 = 7.5, so 1% = 7.5 people and 7.5 × 28 = 210 (refer to Test 2 Q 8 on dividing by powers of 10 Test 18 Q 6 on multiplying decimals).

6 **45** Find the total of matches they drew and lost: 4 + 6 + 8 = 18; 12 + 8 + 7 = 27; and 18 + 27 = 45.

7 **38** Begin with the first column: 58 + 19 = 77 and 117 − 77 = 40. Then complete the top two rows: 40 + 18 = 58 and 117 − 58 = 59; 58 + 20 = 78 and 117 − 78 = 39. Finally, complete the last two columns: 18 + 39 = 57 and 117 − 57 = 60; 59 + 20 = 79 and 117 − 79 = 38. Check by calculating the bottom row: 19 + 60 = 79 and 117 − 79 = 38.

8 **15** Refer to Test 12 Q 2 on using conversion graphs: the temperature is increasing in increments of 1°C; the number of ice creams is going up in increments of 5 every 2 squares.

9 $\frac{1}{2}$ or 0.5 or 50% Refer to Test Qs 6–10 on probability. There are 8 possible outcomes and a total of 4 odd numbers, i.e., $\frac{4}{8}$ and can be simplified to $\frac{1}{2}$ (refer to Test 1 Q 1). 0.5 or 50% is also acceptable as they are both equivalents of $\frac{1}{2}$.

10 **E** Look at the box opposite to help decide. The missing option needs to be a question about the type of car, with the answer of 'YES' if it is a blue saloon and 'NO' if it is a blue sports car. Therefore 'Is it a saloon?' is the only option that works here.

Puzzle 1 (page 42)

204

a **8 different sizes** There are 8 rows and columns, therefore 8 different sizes.

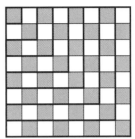

b **8 × 8 = 64 of the 1 by 1 squares**
c **1 × 1 = 1 of the 8 × 8 squares**
  2 × 2 = 4 of the 7 by 7 squares
  3 × 3 = 9 of the 6 by 6 squares
  4 × 4 = 16 of the 5 by 5 squares
  5 × 5 = 25 of the 4 by 4 squares
  6 × 6 = 36 of the 3 by 3 squares
  7 × 7 = 49 of the 2 by 2 squares
  1 + 4 + 9 + 16 + 25 + 36 + 49 = 140

Puzzle 2 (page 43)

a **1, 4, 9, 16, 25**
Complete a table to keep a tally of the lights going on and off. The first few are shown below.

Care-taker	Office 1	Office 2	Office 3	Office 4	Office 5	Office 6	Office 7	Office 8	Office 9	Office 10	Office 11	Office 12
1	OFF	OFF	OFF	OFF	OFF	OFF	OFF	OFF	OFF	OFF	OFF	OFF
2		ON		ON		ON		ON		ON		ON
3			ON			OFF			ON			OFF
4				OFF				OFF				ON

b Square numbers Refer to Test 5 Qs 1–4 on square numbers.

Puzzle 3 (page **44**)

	1	2			5	5	
5		3	6		2	7	
6	5		6	1			7
	8	7		9	1		
4		4	3		4	9	
2	9		8	3		2	
	6	7		4	8		

Refer to: Test 5 Qs 1–4 on square and cubed numbers; Test 13 Q 6 on multiples; Test 4 Q 7 on prime numbers.

Across

1 A dozen is twelve. 3 $110 \div 2 = 55$
6 $6^2 = 6 \times 6 = 36$
8 $3^3 = 3 \times 3 \times 3 = 27$ 10 $5 \times 13 = 65$
12 $5^2 = 25$ and $6^2 = 36$: $25 + 36 = 61$
14 $7^2 = 49$: $36 + 49 + 2 = 87$
16 $102 - 11 = 91$ 19 $37 + 6 = 43$
21 $7^2 = 49$
23 $2^2 = 4$ and $5^2 = 25$: $4 + 25 = 29$
25 $100 - 17 = 83$
27 $60 + 7 = 67$ 28 $51 - 3 = 48$

Down

2 23 4 $23 + 29 = 52$
5 $7 \times 8 = 56$ 7 $6 \times 11 = 66$
9 $7 \times 11 = 77$, so 77 is divisible by 7 and 11 as well.
11 $79 - 21 = 58$ 13 $1 \times 19 = 19$
15 $2 \times 37 = 74$ 17 14lbs = 1 stone
18 $2 \times 21 = 42$ 20 $2 \times 19 = 38$
22 $4 \times 23 = 92$
24 $10^2 - 2^2 = 100 - 4 = 96$
26 $2 \times 17 = 34$, therefore 34 is divisible by 17, $34 \div 17 = 2$

Puzzle 4 (page **45**)

 = 5   = 8   =9

				30
				27
				31
				26

34	20	**30**	**30**

Begin with the column showing 4 dogs = 20: $20 \div 4 = 5$, so each dog represents 5. The bottom row shows 2 dogs and 2 cats, so work this one out next: 2 dogs = 10 and $26 - 10 = 16$. Therefore if 2 cats = 16, 1 cat = 8. Then work out the second row: $5 + 8 + 5 = 18$, so subtract this from 27 to find the number the owl represents ($27 - 18 = 9$). Use this information to work out the rest of the missing numbers.

Puzzle 5 (page **46**)

1 kg, 2 kg, 4 kg, 8 kg, 16 kg
Create a table to keep tally. A 1 kg weight is needed to make 1 kg, so Box 1 is 1 kg. The only way 2 kg can be made is with 2×1 kg weights or 1×2 kg weight: as the boxes cannot be the same weight, Box 2 must be 2 kg. Boxes 1 and 2 can then be used to make 3 kg. The only way to make 4 kg is with 2×2 kg or 1 kg + 3 kg, however, there is only one of each weight and no 3 kg weight to use, so Box 3 must be 4 kg. 5 kg can then be made using Boxes 1 and 3 (1 kg + 4 kg = 5 kg), 6 kg can be made using Boxes 2 and 3 (2 kg + 4 kg) and so on. The beginning of the table is shown on the right: continue the pattern until 31 kg is reached.

Weight	Weights used
1 kg	1 kg
2 kg	2 kg
3 kg	1 kg + 2 kg
4 kg	4 kg
5 kg	1 kg + 4 kg
6 kg	2 kg + 4 kg
7 kg	1 kg + 2 kg + 4 kg
8 kg	8kg
9 kg	1 kg + 8 kg
10 kg	2 kg + 8 kg
11 kg	1 kg + 2 kg + 8 kg
12 kg	4 kg + 8 kg
13 kg	1 kg + 4 kg + 8 kg
14 kg	2 kg + 4 kg + 8 kg
15 kg	1 kg + 2 kg + 4 kg + 8 kg
16 kg	16 kg

5

Here is part of a conversion table. Which figure is missing from the table?

ft	m
5	1.53
6	1.83
7	2.13
8	2.44

m	ft
5	16.40
6	?
7	22.97
8	26.25

Circle the answer.

A 18.23 ft

B 19.01 ft

C 19.68 ft

D 15.33 ft

E 16.40 ft

6

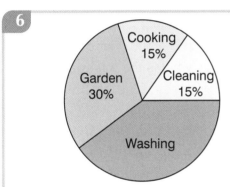

Of 55 households surveyed, how many used most of their water for washing?

_____

7

What is the perimeter of the room?

_____ m

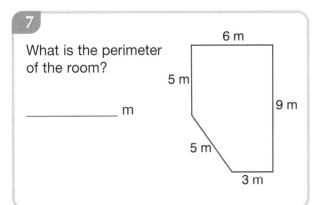

8

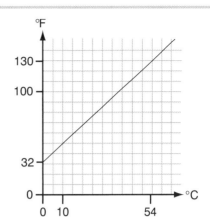

Look at the graph to show the temperature conversion between Fahrenheit (°F) and Celsius (°C).

Use your graph to work out how many degrees Fahrenheit are equivalent to 30° Celsius.

Circle the answer.

A 0   **B** 90   **C** 80   **D** 86   **E** 76

9

Iris withdraws £1300 from her bank account.

She is given the money in £20 notes.

How many £20 notes does she have in total?

_____

10

Which circle contains only multiples of either 3 or 5?

Circle the answer.

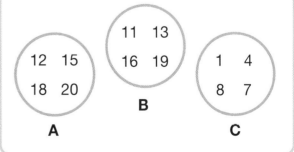

Total [____]

TEST 19: **Mixed**

1

The probability that Mr Yang will catch the bus to school is 0.4.

The probability he will walk is 0.2.

Otherwise he will drive to school.

What is the chance that he will drive to school?

_____

2

A piece of wood 6 m 18 cm long is to be cut into three equal pieces.

How long will each piece be?

Circle the answer.

A 3 m 6 cm   **B** 2 m 60 cm   **C** 3 m 0.6 cm

D 306 m   **E** 206 cm

3

NOZ   ONS   NSO   ZNO   NOS

Which of these makes a word when rotated through 180°?

Circle the correct word.

4

What fraction of 3 hours is 45 minutes?

_____

5

Jen wants to save two files onto a USB stick.

One file is 68 MB. The other is 96 MB.

A USB stick can hold 650 MB.

How many MB of space will be left on the USB stick once she has saved both files?

_____

6

Reflecting this scalene triangle in its dashed side, will make a quadrilateral.

What is the name of this quadrilateral?

Circle the answer.

A Square   **B** Rectangle   **C** Rhombus

D Parallelogram   **E** Kite

7

If $4x - 2 = 2x + 8$, what is the value of x?

_____

8

Daxa buys two 1.5 litre cartons of juice, 3 litres of milk and a 500 g jar of coffee.

Approximately what is the total weight of the shopping?

Circle the answer.

A 0.5 kg   **B** 1.5 kg   **C** 2.5 kg

D 5.5 kg   **E** 6.5 kg

9

Amanda plants 17 rows and 13 columns of cabbage plants in a rectangular pattern.

How many cabbage plants has she planted altogether?

_____

10

? → [   ] → 94

This machine triples and then adds 7.

Which number has been put in?

_____

26

Total [   ]

TEST 20: **Mixed**

1

$$\frac{1}{4} \quad \frac{3}{8} \quad \frac{2}{5} \quad \frac{2}{7} \quad \frac{7}{32}$$

Which of these fractions has the lowest value?

Circle the answer.

2

Given that $3x + 9y = 6z$,

what is the value of $x + 3y = ?$

Give the answer in terms of z.

_____

3

When the net is folded to make the cuboid, which corner will join to corner L?

_____

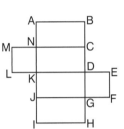

4

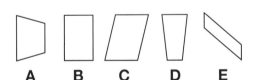

A   B   C   D   E

Which quadrilateral does not have an obtuse angle?

Circle the answer.

5

In Grange School, girls and boys are in the ratio 8 : 9.

There are 72 boys, how many girls are there?

_____

6

Norbert is 2 metres 0 centimetres tall. Which is the closest to his height in feet and inches?

Circle the answer.

A 5 feet 11 inches   **B** 6 feet 1 inch

C 6 feet 3 inches   **D** 6 feet 5 inches

E 6 feet 7 inches

7

Find the coordinates of points P, Q and R.

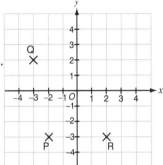

P (___, ___)

Q (___, ___)

R (___, ___)

8

£420 is raised at a Funday.

$\frac{6}{7}$ of the money is donated to charity.

The rest is kept as profit.

How much profit is made?

_____

9 $4x - 2y = z.$

Find the value of x when $y = 7$ and $z = 2$.

_____

10

121 → ÷11 — ×12 → _____

Complete the function machine.

Total [   ]

1

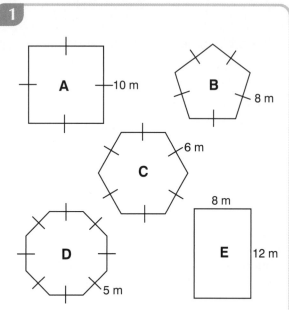

Which shape has a different perimeter from the others?

_____

2

Reflecting this right-angled triangle in its dashed side will make another triangle.

What is the name of this triangle?

Circle the answer.

A Equilateral

B Scalene

C Isosceles

D Right-angled

E Regular

3

Lauren was carrying a 620 g bag of potatoes, and two 200 g bags of fruit.

The total weight of Peter's bags was exactly half the total weight of Lauren's bags.

How much weight did Peter carry?

_____ g

4

Miss Drake is 6 feet 0 inches tall.

Which is the closest to her height in metres?

Circle the answer.

A 1.7 m   **B** 1.8 m   **C** 1.9 m

D 2.0 m   **E** 2.1 m

5

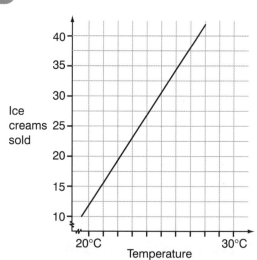

How many ice creams were sold when the temperature was 26°C?

_____

6

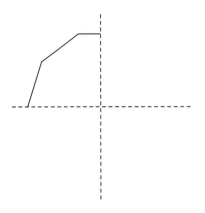

The diagram shows part of a shape and two lines of symmetry.

What is the name of the complete shape?

Circle the answer.

A Regular hexagon

B Regular octagon

C Regular dodecagon

D Regular decagon

E Irregular dodecagon

7

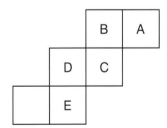

Look at this net of a closed cube.

Which side will be directly opposite the unmarked side, when it is folded to make the cube?

Circle the answer.

A   **B**   **C**   **D**   **E**

8

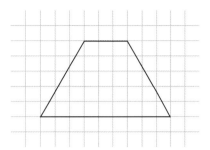

In the diagram above 1 square represents 1 cm².

What is the area of the trapezium?

_____ cm²

9

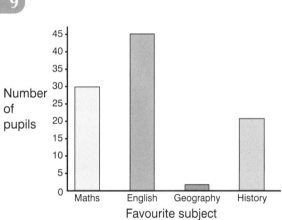

How many people like the most popular subject?

_____

10

May pays a £700 deposit towards a car costing £3899.

She saves £457 per month toward the total cost.

How many months does it take her to save the rest of the money?

_____

Total

TEST 22: **Mixed**

1

In which number is the 7 worth seven hundred?
Circle the answer.

A 70 608   **B** 83 768   **C** 1127

D 103 872   **E** 47 316

2

What fraction of 1 hour is 40 minutes?
Leave your answer in its simplest form.

_____

3

$5 \times 5 \times 5 \times 5 \times 5 \times 5 = ?$
Circle the answer.

A 5^6 **B** 30   **C** 6^5 **D** 555 555   **E** 56

4

The sides labelled x are the same length.
How many times will the small right-angled triangle fit into the octagon?

_____

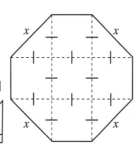

5

Ian sends 12 text messages daily costing 4p each.
He makes 4 calls each day costing 20p each.
How much does he spend altogether over five days?

_____

6

Which of these has a horizontal line of symmetry?
Circle the answer.

HIM   MIM   TIM   LIN   HIH

7

Cindy has to pay £1 to enter a fair.
She only has one type of coin.
Circle the option which she could not use.

A One £1 coin   **B** Two 50p coins

C Four 25p coins   **D** Five 20p coins

E Ten 10p coins

8

The area of a square is 64 cm².
What is the perimeter of the square?
Circle the answer.

A 16 cm   **B** 9 cm   **C** 32 cm

D 50 cm   **E** 64 cm

9

The probability it will snow on Christmas Day 2020 is 0.02.
What is the chance it will not snow on Christmas Day 2020?

_____

10

What is the area of the shape?

_____ m²

6 m   7 m
4 m   4 m
8 m
18 m

30

Total

Test time: 0 | | | | | 5 | | | | | 10 minutes

1

What is the six in the number 7608 worth?

_____

2

Una sells ice lollies for 45p and ice cream cones for 32p.

She sells 34 of the ice lollies and 12 cones.

How much does she make altogether?

£_____

3

The perimeter of a rectangle is 50 cm. If the rectangle is 20 cm long, what is the area of the rectangle?

Circle the answer.

A 40 cm²   **B** 70 cm²   **C** 60 cm²

D 250 cm²   **E** 100 cm²

4

Which ratio is not the same as the ratio 14 : 20?

Circle the answer.

A 7 : 10   **B** $2 : \frac{20}{7}$ **C** $1 : \frac{10}{7}$

D 28 : 40   **E** 10 : 16

5

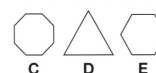

A   **B**   **C**   **D**   **E**

An angle inside a polygon is called an interior angle.

Which one of the above regular polygons has an interior angle of 135°?

Circle the answer.

6

A train leaves London at 13.47. The journey to Leeds takes 2 hours and 29 minutes.

What time does it arrive in Leeds?

_____

7

Which number is divisible by 12 and 24? Circle the answer.

A 12   **B** 36   **C** 48   **D** 60   **E** 80

8

Find the size of the unmarked angle.

_____ °

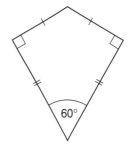

60°

9

Jennie collected money for a charity.

One morning she received the following donations:

£1.64   £2.12   £0.89   20p   £3.45

She collected £34 in the afternoon.

How much did she collect in total?

_____

10

Which of the following fractions has the smallest value?

Circle the answer.

$\frac{2}{3}$ $\frac{4}{10}$ $\frac{5}{8}$ $\frac{1}{6}$ $\frac{7}{10}$

Total

Test 24: **Mixed**

1

Which of the following has the largest value?

Circle the answer.

$\frac{5}{7}$ 71%   0.69 $\frac{2}{3}$ 65%

2

What number does the arrow point to?

_____

3

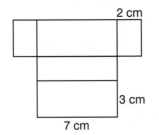

Find the size of the angle marked x in this isosceles triangle.

_____ °

4

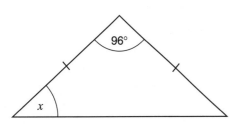

This is a net of an open cuboid.
It is then folded to make an open box.
What is the volume of the box?

_____ cm³

5

Mike is using a map where 1 cm represents 2 km.
His walk is 8 cm on the map.
How far will his actual walk be?

_____ km

6

Name	Bank Balance
Mr Spend	−£145
Mr Save	−£468
Mr Broke	£12
Mr Rich	£567
Mr Debt	−£222
Miss Out	£879

The table above shows the balance of six people's bank accounts.
Who owes the most money?

_____

7

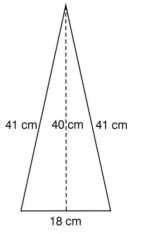

What is the area of the triangle?

_____ cm²

32

8

Guide the car along the white squares on the plan from the start to the finish.

It can only move FORWARD, TURN RIGHT 90° and TURN LEFT 90°.

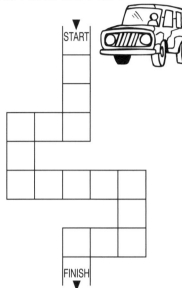

Circle the correct instructions.

A FORWARD 3, TURN LEFT 90°,
FORWARD 3, TURN LEFT 90°,
FORWARD 2, TURN LEFT 90°,
FORWARD 4, TURN RIGHT 90°,
FORWARD 2, TURN RIGHT 90°,
FORWARD 2, TURN LEFT 90°,
FORWARD 1

B FORWARD 3, TURN RIGHT 90°,
FORWARD 2, TURN LEFT 90°,
FORWARD 2, TURN LEFT 90°,
FORWARD 4, TURN RIGHT 90°,
FORWARD 2, TURN RIGHT 90°,
FORWARD 2, TURN LEFT 90°,
FORWARD 1

C FORWARD 3, TURN LEFT 90°,
FORWARD 3, TURN LEFT 90°,
FORWARD 2, TURN LEFT 90°,
FORWARD 4, TURN LEFT 90°,
FORWARD 2, TURN RIGHT 90°,
FORWARD 3, TURN LEFT 90°,
FORWARD 1

D FORWARD 3, TURN RIGHT 90°,
FORWARD 2, TURN LEFT 90°,
FORWARD 2, TURN LEFT 90°,
FORWARD 4, TURN RIGHT 90°,
FORWARD 2, TURN RIGHT 90°,
FORWARD 3, TURN RIGHT 90°,
FORWARD 1

E FORWARD 3, TURN RIGHT 90°,
FORWARD 2, TURN LEFT 90°,
FORWARD 2, TURN LEFT 90°,
FORWARD 4, TURN RIGHT 90°,
FORWARD 2, TURN LEFT 90°,
FORWARD 2, TURN RIGHT 90°,
FORWARD 1

9

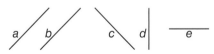

Which of the statements is correct?

Circle the answer.

A b and c are parallel

B a and b are vertical

C e is vertical

D d is horizontal

E a and b are parallel

10

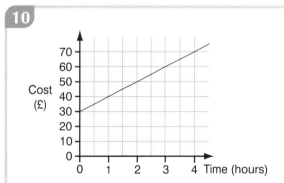

How much does Ben charge for a plumbing job lasting 4 hours?

_____

Time for a break! Go to Puzzle Page 45 ▶

(**33**)

Total

TEST 25: **Mixed**

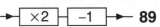

1

Which number completes the list in order of size?

    0.038, ...,   0.042

Circle the answer.

0.0379   0.4   0.04   0.004   0.39

2

A submarine descends from sea level (0 m) to a depth of 150 m.

It then rises 76 m.

How far is it below sea level now?

_____ m below sea level.

3

Which of these makes a word when rotated through 180°?

Circle the answer.

NOOS   ENO   ONNS   ENNA   OOB

4

Which answer is different from the others?

Circle the answer.

A 0.1 of 20   **B** 10% of 20   **C** $\frac{1}{10}$ of 20

D 20% of 10   **E** 0.01 of 20

5

How many Fentos are equivalent to 25 Pentos?

_____ Fentos

6

Complete the function machine.

_____ → ×2 → −1 → **89**

7

This is a net of an open cube.

It is folded to make an open box.

What is the volume of the box?

_____ cm³

10 cm

8

Which two of these polygons have diagonals that cross at right angles?

Circle the answers.

A Trapezium   **B** Square

C Rhombus   **D** Regular pentagon

E Rectangle

9

Which is the first number greater than 100 that is divisible by both 3 and 6?

_____

10

Jake is driving at a speed of 64 kmh or 40 mph.

Lee is cycling at a speed of 32 kmh or 20 mph.

Roger is travelling on a motorbike at a speed of 96 kmh.

What is his speed in mph?

_____ mph

Total

TEST 26: **Mixed**

Test time: 0 — 5 — 10 minutes

1

0   2   4

What number does the arrow point to?

_____

2

Complete the function machine.

72 → | ÷6 | → | ×15 | → _____

3

Which of the following will hold about 5 ml?
Circle the answer.

A a teaspoon   **B** a swimming pool

C a mug   **D** a bucket

E a reservoir

4

The area of a rectangle is 30 cm².
Which could be the perimeter of the rectangle?
Circle the answer.

A 6 cm   **B** 9 cm   **C** 12 cm

D 22 cm   **E** 28 cm

5

What is the difference between 9°C and −2°C?

_____ °C

6   **5.9945**

Write this number to two decimal places.

_____

7

A school sells 700 concert tickets for £3.99 each.
How much money did they raise?

_____

8

Sue thinks of a positive number, multiplies it by itself and then halves the answer.
The number she ends up with is 18.
What was her original number?

_____

9

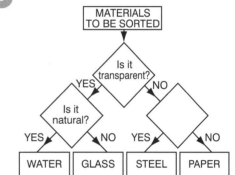

What is missing from the decision tree?
Circle the answer.

A IT IS WEAK.   **B** IT IS STRONG.

C IT IS TRANSPARENT.   **D** Is it strong?

E Is it opaque?

10

In a maths test Andy gets 30 out of the 35 questions correct.
What proportion has he got right?
Circle the answer.

$\frac{5}{7}$ $\frac{6}{7}$ $\frac{3}{5}$ $\frac{3}{4}$ $\frac{5}{6}$

(35)

Total

TEST 27: **Mixed**

1

A map has a scale of 1 : 25 000.

What does 4 cm on the map represent in actual distance?

Circle the answer.

A 25 m

B 25 km

C 100 m

D 100 km

E 1 km

2

| 1 | 2 | 3 | 4 | 5 |

Which of the statements is incorrect?

Circle the answer.

A 2, 3 and 5 are parallel

B 2, 3 and 5 are vertical

C 1 and 4 are parallel

D 1 is perpendicular to 2

E 5 is horizontal

3

The time in Thornsburg is 6 hours ahead of London.

The time in London is 8.27 pm.

What is the time in Thornsburg?

Circle the answer.

A 2.27 pm   **B** 14.27

C 02.27 pm   **D** 02.27

E 14.27 am

4

Guide the robot through the grid without hitting any animals.

He can only move FORWARD, TURN LEFT 90° and TURN RIGHT 90°.

Circle the correct instructions.

A FORWARD 4, TURN LEFT 90°, FORWARD 1, TURN RIGHT 90°, FORWARD 1

B FORWARD 1, TURN LEFT 90°, FORWARD 2, TURN RIGHT 90°, FORWARD 2, TURN RIGHT 90°, FORWARD 1, TURN LEFT 90°, FORWARD 2

C FORWARD 1, TURN LEFT 90°, FORWARD 2, TURN RIGHT 90°, FORWARD 2, TURN RIGHT 90°, FORWARD 2, TURN LEFT 90°, FORWARD 1

D FORWARD 2, TURN LEFT 90°, FORWARD 2, TURN RIGHT 90°, FORWARD 2, TURN RIGHT 90°, FORWARD 1, TURN LEFT 90°, FORWARD 1

E FORWARD 2, TURN LEFT 90°, FORWARD 2, TURN RIGHT 90°, FORWARD 2, TURN RIGHT 90°, FORWARD 2, TURN LEFT 90°, FORWARD 1

5

An ammeter shows current of 4 amps (A).
There are 1000 mA to 1 amp.
The current drops by 500 mA.
What reading does the ammeter now show?

_____ A

6

Convert the list below to fractions and find the smallest fraction.
Circle the answer.

A 30 minutes as a fraction of 2 hours

B 20 minutes as a fraction of 3 hours

C 15 minutes as a fraction of 2 hours

D 40 minutes as a fraction of 1 hour

E 10 minutes as a fraction of 1 hour

7

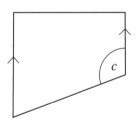

What is the approximate size of the angle marked c in the trapezium?
Circle the answer.

A 150°

B 110°

C 90°

D 60°

E 300°

8

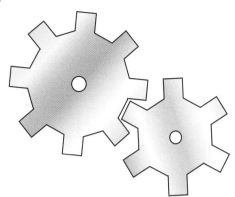

The cog with 8 grooves makes 12 complete revolutions.
How many complete revolutions will the cog with 6 grooves have made?

_____

9

Complete the function machine.

27 → ×7 → ÷3 →

_____

10

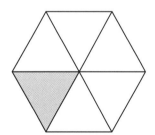

How many more triangles need to be shaded so 50% of the hexagon is shaded?
Circle the answer.

1   2   3   4   5

Total

1

John collected the following data from 100 children.

	Drum	Recorder	Guitar
Boys	3	?	12
Girls	23	18	18

How many boys gave the recorder as their favourite instrument?

_____

2

Lia thinks of a positive number.
She multiplies it by itself and gets 144.
What was the number she started with?

_____

3

14 000 people each pay £25 for a concert ticket.
How much money is raised?

£_____

4

What is the missing number?

135	148	109
122	?	148
109	122	135

_____

5

Out of 600 people interviewed, 378 liked watching soap operas.
What percentage of people surveyed liked watching soap operas?

_____

6

Pat collected the following data from 100 pupils.

	Tennis	Judo	Ballet
Boys	13	1	18
Girls	54	3	?

How many girls gave ballet as their favourite activity?

_____

7

This is a net of an open cuboid.
It is then folded to make an open box.
What is the volume of the box?

_____ cm³

0.3 cm

0.6 cm

0.2 cm

8

A   B   C   D   E

Which shape has 3 edges less than shape D?

_____

9

Lara usually buys 150 g bags of crisps.
She sees a bag which is 30% larger.
What is the weight of the large bag?

_____ g

10

If p is $\frac{3}{4}$ of q, what is $3q$?

_____

Total [   ]

1

The table below shows the atmospheric temperature at different altitudes.

Altitude above sea level (ft)	Temperature (°C)
1 000	10
2 000	8
5 000	2
15 000	−8
20 000	−23
50 000	−67

Which altitude is the coldest?

_____ ft

2

What is the size of the angle marked b in the isosceles triangle?

Circle the answer.

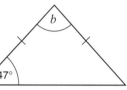

A 266° **B** 86° **C** 96° **D** 47° **E** 153°

3

Mia travels 40 miles before she has a rest.

Her total journey is 50 miles.

What fraction of her journey has she completed?

_____

4

Find the range for the hours of sunshine shown in the table.

Month	May	June	July	Aug	Sep
Hours	172	171	189	197	186

Circle the answer.

A 171 **B** 26 **C** 184 **D** 5 **E** 25

5

Kim is ordering some stationery.

She orders x boxes of pencils each containing 50 pencils.

She orders y boxes of pens each containing 20 pens.

How many items does she order?

Leave your answer in terms of x and y.

_____

6

6.55 ⟶ 6.65

What number does the arrow point to?

_____

7

Headache tablets are sold in packets of 18. How many complete packets can be made from 293 tablets?

_____

8

Which ratio is NOT the same as the ratio 12 : 60? Circle the letter.

A 6 : 30   **B** 2 : 10   **C** 1 : 5

D 5 : 1   **E** 24 : 120

9 1   8   9   15   16

Which is **neither** a square number **nor** a cube number? Circle the answer.

10

The Hundred Years War began in 1337 and finished in 1453. How long did it last?

_____

Total

1

Stu was y years old 13 years ago.
How old will he be in 2 years time?
Leave your answer in terms of y.

_____

2

Key:  = 10 loaves
= 5 loaves

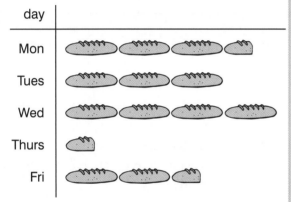

day	
Mon	
Tues	
Wed	
Thurs	
Fri	

The shop almost ran out of stock one day and had to shut early.
Which day do you think this occurred?

_____

3

There are 360 books in the school library.
$\frac{1}{5}$ of the books are fiction.
$\frac{2}{5}$ of the books are non-fiction.
The rest are reference books.
How many reference books are in the library?

_____

4

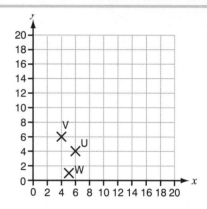

Look at the grid shown.
What are the coordinates of the points U, V and W?
Circle the answer.

A U(6, 4)   V(4, 6)   W(5, 1)

B U(4, 6)   V(6, 4)   W(1, 5)

C U(3, 2)   V(2, 3)   W(2.5, 0.5)

D U(6, 4)   V(4, 6)   W(4, 2)

E U(6, 4)   V(4, 6)   W(6, 2)

5

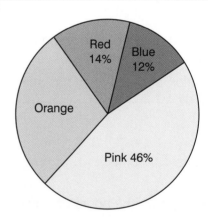

750 people were asked their favourite colour.
The results are displayed in the pie chart.
How many people liked orange?

_____

6

Year	Won	Drawn	Lost
2002	4	4	12
2003	6	6	8
2004	5	8	7

How many matches in total did the table tennis team not win?

_____

7

	18	
58		20
19		?

When every space is filled in, each row and each column adds up to 117.

Which number should replace the question mark?

_____

8

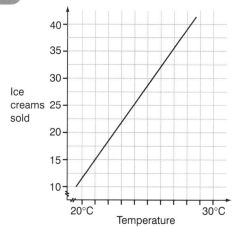

The graph shows the number of ice creams sold depending on the temperature of the day. How many ice creams were sold when the temperature was 21°C?

_____

9

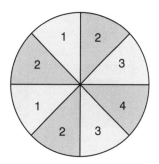

A game is shown above.

Players have to throw a dart at the board and whichever sector (wedge) the dart lands in is their score for that round.

The darts can not land on the borders.

All the throws of the darts are fair.

What is the probability of obtaining an odd number on the throw of the dart?

_____

10

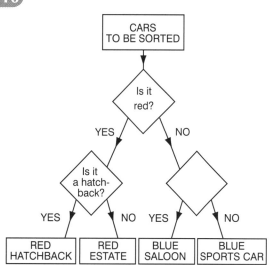

What is missing from the decision tree?
Circle the answer.

A Is it a sports car?

B IT IS A SPORTS CAR.

C Is it blue?

D IT IS BLUE.

E Is it a saloon?

Total

Puzzle ❶

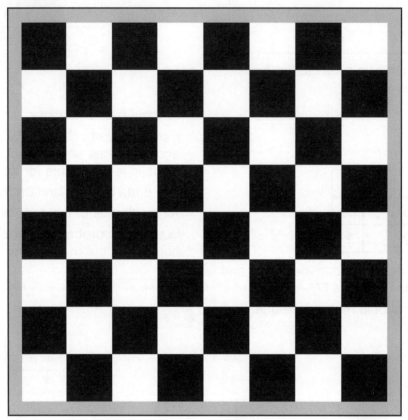

How many squares are on a chessboard? _____

Clues:

a How many different sized squares can you find? _____

b How many of the smallest squares can you find? _____

c How many of the other sizes of squares can you find? _____

Puzzle ❷

An office block has thirty offices
numbered 1, 2, 3, up to 30.

Thirty caretakers work at the offices
and they all flick the light switches before
they leave at the end of the day.

They don't care whether the lights
are on or off.
If the lights are on, they switch them off
and if the lights are off they switch them on!

The first caretaker who leaves, switches
every light off.

The second caretaker who leaves,
flicks every second switch starting with office
number two.

The third caretaker who leaves,
flicks every third switch starting with
office number three.

The fourth caretaker who leaves,
flicks every fourth switch starting with office
number four.

This continues until the thirtieth caretaker
leaves and only flicks the switch in office
number thirty.

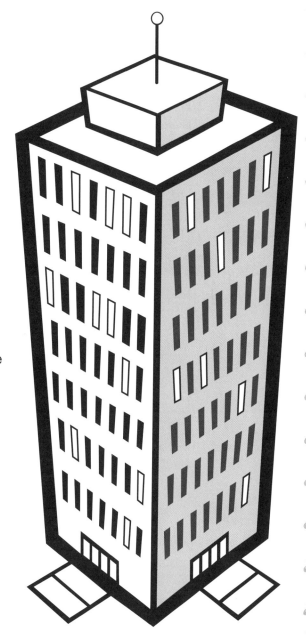

a Which offices are left with the lights off? _____

b What is special about these office numbers? _____

Puzzle ③

Complete the grid by answering the questions below.

	1	2		3	4	
5		6	7		8	9
10	11		12	13		
	14	15		16	17	
18		19	20		21	22
23	24		25	26		
	27			28		

Across

1 a dozen
3 half of one hundred and ten
6 a square number
8 three cubed
10 a multiple of thirteen
12 five squared plus six squared
14 six squared plus seven squared plus two
16 102 − 11
19 37 + 6
21 seven squared
23 two squared plus five squared
25 100 − 17
27 60 + 7
28 51 − 3

Down

2 a prime number
4 23 + 29
5 seven eights
7 a multiple of eleven
9 a number divisible by seven and eleven
11 79 − 21
13 a factor of nineteen
15 a multiple of thirty-seven
17 the number of pounds in a stone
18 double twenty-one
20 a multiple of nineteen
22 a multiple of twenty-three
24 two squared less than ten squared
26 divisible by seventeen

Puzzle 4

The numbers shown are the totals of the four numbers in that row or column.

cat	dog	owl	cat	
owl	dog	cat	dog	27
owl	dog	cat	owl	
cat	dog	dog	cat	26

	20		

Find the remaining totals and write them in the empty total boxes.

45

Puzzle ⑤

Five boxes each hold some one kilogram weights.
No two boxes weigh the same.

Their total weight is 31 kilograms.

It is possible to make any weight up to 31 kilograms using one or more boxes.

How much does each box weigh?

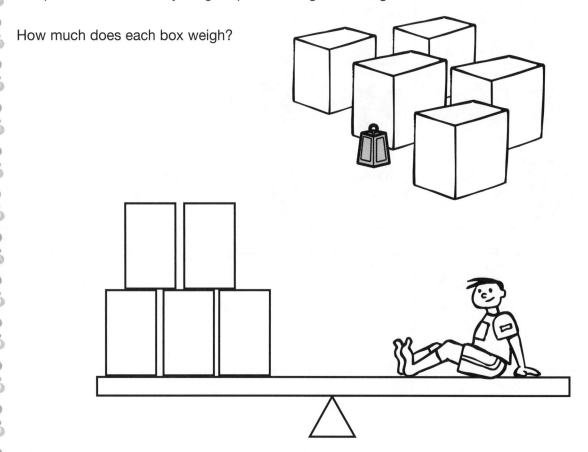

Progress Grid

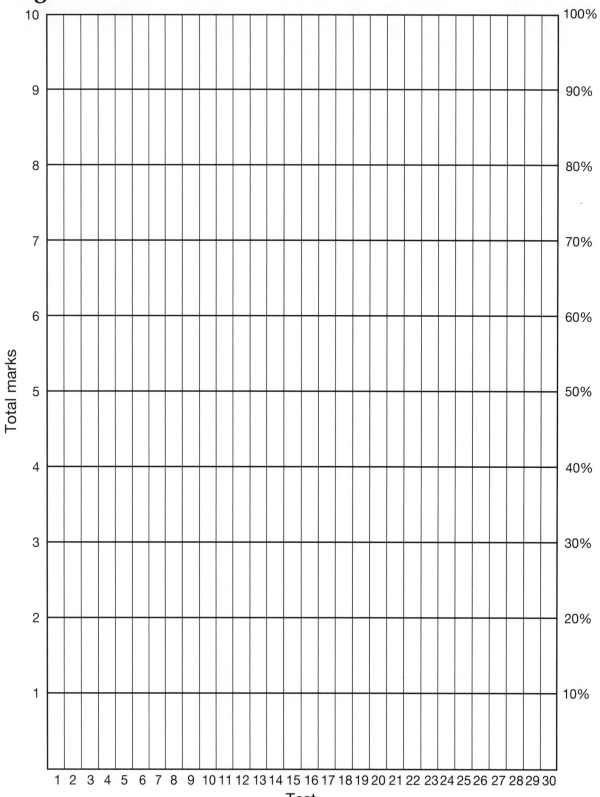

Test

Bond
No.1 for exam success

Verbal Reasoning

10 Minute Tests

10–11+ years

OXFORD
UNIVERSITY PRESS

Underline the two words, one from each group, which are the most opposite in meaning.

Example (dawn, <u>early</u>, wake)   (<u>late</u>, stop, sunrise)

1	(tidy, dust, clean)	(neat, scruffy, brush)
2	(climb, broad, slender)	(narrow, wide, high)
3	(hearty, cough, unwell)	(strong, cold, healthy)
4	(pale, red, coloured)	(flushed, faint, whiten)

Find a word that is similar in meaning to the word in capital letters and that rhymes with the second word.

Example CABLE   tyre   _wire_

5	DEFEND	detect	_____
6	SLICE	fleece	_____
7	KNOT	sigh	_____
8	MINUTE	shiny	_____

Underline the pair of words most opposite in meaning.

Example cup, mug   coffee, milk   <u>hot, cold</u>

9	few, many	some, any	lift, raise
10	silly, foolish	stupid, sensible	serious, kind
11	show, display	conceal, hide	present, absent
12	far, near	distant, horizon	planet, star

Underline the word in brackets closest in meaning to the word in capitals.

Example UNHAPPY   (unkind, death, laughter, <u>sad</u>, friendly)

13	QUIET	(almost, noisy, busy, silence, thought)
14	CLASS	(children, work, school, student, group)
15	TEAR	(shred, drop, cries, sad, prick)
16	QUERY	(answer, question, peculiar, same, reply)

Look at the pair of words on the left. Underline the one word in the brackets that goes with the word outside the brackets in the same way as the first two words go together.

Example good, better   bad, (naughty, worst, <u>worse</u>, nasty)

17	upset, cry	happy, (pleased, sad, growl, laugh)
18	left, right	for, (five, with, against, hand)
19	finger, wrist	toe, (foot, ankle, leg, nail)
20	reveal, show	retain, (return, get, stop, keep)

2

Total

Underline the one word in brackets which will go equally well with both the pairs of words outside the brackets.

Example rush, attack   cost, fee   (price, hasten, strike, <u>charge</u>, money)

1 talon, pincer   scratch, tear   (rake, nail, foot, claw)
2 even, flat   position, stage   (level, dull, horizontal, period)
3 pour, empty out   end, furthest point (overbalance, apex, tip, fall)
4 site, situation   put, allocate   (location, place, circumstance, move)
5 clean, clear   innocent, virtuous   (pure, not guilty, harmless, hygienic)

Rearrange the muddled words in capital letters in the following sentences so that they make sense.

Example There are sixty SNODCES __*seconds*__ in a UTMINE ___*minute*___.

6 She put the picnic KSATEB _____ on the CHKTINE _____ table.
7 It is cold DSIOUET _____ so put your KJATCE _____ on.
8 Straight after our SHILENG _____ SNOLES _____, we had French.
9 Our local BRALIYR _____ has a RAVIDE _____ selection of books.
10 In the OLOHSC _____ holidays, we went PNIGMCA _____ in Wales.

Rearrange the letters in capitals to make another word. The new word has something to do with the first two words or phrases.

Example spot   soil   SAINT   ___*STAIN*___

11 prickle   splinter   NORTH   _____
12 clutch   grip   SCALP   _____
13 cry   complaint   TABLE   _____
14 beat   pulse   BROTH   _____
15 jeans   material   MINED   _____

Find and underline the two words that need to change places for each sentence to make sense.

Example She went to <u>letter</u> the <u>write</u>.

16 The door sign has fallen off the toilet.
17 You have arrived time in just for tea.
18 Why have you put your feet on the wrong shoes?
19 In a park, the storm bench was blown over.
20 The autumn fall during the leaves.

Total

TEST 3: Selecting Words

Which one letter can be added to the front of all of these words to make new words?

Example _Care_   _Cat_   _Crate_   _Call_   _Clip_

1   __age   __ally   __at   __oar   __each

2   __ice   __an   __alley   __omit   __ow

3   __hunk   __lash   __hip   __rush   __raft

4   __ash   __align   __utter   __eat   __ail

Find two letters that will end the first word and start the second word.

Example   pas (_t_ _a_) ste

5   squ (__ __) ea   6   spa (__ __) ally

7   twi (__ __) op   8   bo (__ __) orn

Underline two words, one from each group, that go together to form a new word. The word in the first group always comes first.

Example   (hand, <u>green</u>, for)   (light, <u>house</u>, sure)

9   (fourth, pass, trouble)   (with, some, by)

10   (in, out, on)   (too, shirt, vest)

11   (bear, bore, be)   (ring, gun, for)

12   (for, end, first)   (rest, less, tale)

Underline the word in brackets that goes best with the words given outside the brackets.

Example   word, paragraph, sentence   (pen, cap, <u>letter</u>, top, stop)

13   road, street, avenue   (town, lane, footpath, car, walk)

14   toes, ankle, heel   (son, hand, stocking, foot, wrist)

15   ruler, rubber, pencil   (lesson, case, pen, book, school)

16   sandal, slipper, boot   (socks, glove, person, hat, trainer)

Underline the one word in each group that can be made from the letters of the word in capital letters.

Example   CHAMPION   camping   notch   peach   cramp   <u>chimp</u>

17   PARTICLE   patch   crate   prick   letter   treat

18   MONSTER   mower   stare   stone   moist   stream

19   COUPLES   place   supple   plush   scoop   slope

20   FLOUNDER   drown   folder   friend   drain   floor

Total

Write the four-letter word hidden at the end of one word and the beginning of the next word. The order of the letters may not be changed.

Example   We had ba<u>ts and</u> balls.   ___sand___

1   A long icicle appeared on her windowsill last night.   _____

2   The ghostly sound of both owls could be heard.   _____

3   My cousins have stones all around their pond.   _____

4   In an airport lounge any unattended parcel looks suspicious. _____

5   Pour the cream into the striped jug please.   _____

Find the three-letter word that can be added to the letters in capitals to make a new word. The new word will complete the sentence sensibly. Write the three-letter word.

Example   The cat sprang onto the MO.   ___USE___

6   In our pond we have a WR feature.   _____

7   Maisy's VAGE has pretty thatched cottages.   _____

8   There is a zebra CROSG right by our school.   _____

9   Toby's rabbit is white with red E.   _____

10   In class, we put up our hands before SKING.   _____

Find a word that can be put in front of each of the following words to make a new, compound word.

Example   cast   fall   ward   pour   ___down___

11   market   model   natural   star   _____

12   thing   how   what   body   _____

13   witness   shadow   brow   ball   _____

14   drop   coat   forest   bow   _____

15   guard   boat   style   time   _____

Move one letter from the first word to the second word to make two new words.

Example   hunt   sip   ___hut___   ___snip___

16   bread   tint   _____   _____

17   bung   amble   _____   _____

18   want   pin   _____   _____

19   bridle   growing   _____   _____

20   whine   heart   _____   _____

Total [   ]

TEST 5: **Alphabetical Order and Substitution** Test time: 0 | | | | | 5 | | | | | 10 minutes

If these words were put into alphabetical order, which word would come third?

1	called	curries	charge	colour	circle	_____
2	quaver	quarry	quilts	queen	quartz	_____
3	dragon	dreams	drowsy	drench	drinks	_____
4	planet	placed	palace	pandas	pillow	_____
5	galaxy	gables	garden	gained	gallop	_____

If p = 10, q = 4, r = 3, s = 6, t = 2 and u = 24, find the value of the following.

6 (p + r) − s = _____

7 ps = _____

8 $\left(\frac{u}{q}\right) \times s =$ _____

9 (u − p) + (s − q) = _____

Using the same values as above, write the answers as letters.

10 (u − q) − p = _____

11 qrt = _____

12 pr − s = _____

13 $q^2 − p =$ _____

14 $\frac{qs}{u} + t =$ _____

15 $\frac{s + u}{p} =$ _____

If A = 1, E = 2, L = 3, P = 4, S = 5 and T = 6, find the values of these words when the letters are added together.

16 PLEASE _____

17 PLEAT _____

18 LEAST _____

19 STAPLE _____

Using the same values as above, work out the value of this calculation.

20 LAPSE − PALE _____

(6)

Total [   ]

TEST 6: **Word Progressions**

Look at the first group of three words. The word in the middle has been made from the two other words. Complete the second group of three words in the same way, making a new word in the middle of the group.

Example   PAIN   INTO   TOOK   ALSO   _SOON_   ONLY

1	GRIN	GRIP	PINK	PLUG	_____	NAVE
2	TIME	MILK	LOOK	SLED	_____	SORE
3	PAST	SPOT	TORN	ROTA	_____	YAWN
4	DUMB	BULB	LOBE	LAWN	_____	VEER

Change the first word into the last word by changing one letter at a time and making two new, different words in the middle.

Example   CASE   _CASH_   _WASH_   WISH

5	ZOOM	_____	_____	LOCK
6	TUBE	_____	_____	CARE
7	GOAT	_____	_____	BEAN
8	SORT	_____	_____	FIRM
9	DIET	_____	_____	PART
10	TIME	_____	_____	SAFE

Change the first word of the third pair in the same way as the other pairs to give a new word.

Example   bind, hind   bare, hare   but, _hut_

11	rage, role	page, pole	sage, _____
12	lead, loud	tear, tour	beat, _____
13	shaves, have	tablet, able	misled, _____
14	stream, team	chrome, home	stroll, _____

Find the missing number by using the two numbers outside the brackets in the same way as the other sets of numbers.

Example   2 [8] 4   3[18]6   5 [_25_] 5

15	7 [28] 4	6 [18] 3	9 [__] 5	16	4 [10] 1	3 [18] 6	5 [__] 7
17	7 [1] 7	6 [2] 3	12 [__] 4	18	5 [10] 4	3 [14] 8	2 [__] 6
19	4 [7] 3	9 [17] 8	11 [__] 6	20	6 [10] 2	5 [12] 3	2 [__] 1

Total

Test time: 0   5   10 minutes

Tom had six lessons in different classrooms. Match the lessons he studied with the six unshaded rooms.

Tom studied English in a classroom with a lower number than the one he used for French.

History was in the classroom, directly across the corridor, opposite the classroom for Geography.

5	4	3	2	1

C O R R I D O R

10	9	8	7	6

Maths was in between and next door to Geography and Science.

1–6 Room 1 = _____   Room 3 = _____   Room 4 = _____

Room 5 = _____   Room 7 = _____   Room 8 = _____

From the information supplied, answer the questions.

An explorer was in a dilemma. He needed to travel north-west to his camp. In between was a large crocodile infested swamp. If he travelled west and then north, he would encounter an impenetrable jungle.

What would the explorer encounter:

7   south of the camp? _____   **8**   east of the camp? _____

In which direction would the explorer have to start to go if he decided to:

9   go over the mountains towards the camp?   _____

10   go through the jungle towards the camp?   _____

11   go through the swamp towards the camp?   _____

Class 6S were collecting information to make a graph on the pets owned by the class.

Rabbits were owned by Darren, William, Sita, Jane and Phil.
Sita, Brett, Jane and Sven all had goldfish. All those who owned a goldfish
also had a cat, except Sven. William and Darren also had a dog.
Sandy, William and Brett each had a gerbil. Phil and Sita had a tortoise.

12   How many types of pet are mentioned?   _____

13–14 What pets does Darren have?   _____ _____

15   How many children are mentioned?   _____

16–17 Which two children only have one pet each?   _____ _____

18   Who has a dog and a gerbil?   _____

19   Who has a cat and a gerbil?   _____

20   Who has the most pets?   _____

Total

TEST 8: **Simple Codes**

Test time: 0 |||||||||| 5 ||||||||| 10 minutes

The code for the word COMPUTER is 72384169. Encode each of these words using the same code.

1 TRUE _____

2 RUMP _____

Decode these words using the same code as above.

3 3296 _____

4 8291 _____

If the code for SPENT is ORJAZ, what word is:

5 AJOZ _____

6 OZJR _____

If the code for CALMER is $+x£–@, what would be the code for:

7 MALE _____

8 RACE _____

Match the right word to each code given below.
TEST   MAST   TAME   STEM

9 4617 _____   **10** 4734 _____

11 3471 _____   **12** 1634 _____

Decode these words using the same code as above.

13 7634 _____   **14** 1764 _____

Here are the codes for four words.
9mQ%   mX%3   3Xm9   %Qm9
Match the right code to each word.

15 TURN _____   **16** RATS _____

17 STAR _____   **18** NUTS _____

Encode these words using the same code as above.

19 STUNT _____

20 SATURN _____

9

Total

TEST 9: More Complicated Codes

Test time: 0 5 10 minutes

A B C D E F G H I J K L M N O P Q R S T U V W X Y Z

The word FOOTBALL is written in a code as GPPUCBMM. Using the same code:

1 encode the word SOCCER. ______________

2 decode HPBM. ______________

The word TYPE is written in code as VARG. Encode these words using the same code.

3 JAM ______________

4 ZEBRA ______________

The word FAST is written in code as CXPQ. Encode these words using the same code.

5 TABLE ______________

6 PINK ______________

Decode these words using the same code as above.

7 MXOQ ______________

8 GXAB ______________

The word BEAD is written in code as 2514. Encode these words using the same code.

9 FEED ______________

10 CAGE ______________

11 HEAD ______________

Decode these words using the same code as above.

12 6135 ______________ **13** 85475 ______________

14 If the code for RIGHT is WNLMY, what is the code for LEFT? ______________

The code for the word BLACK is eodfn. Using the same code, pick the correct codes for these words.
sodq odun edun sodb

15 BARK ______________ **16** PLAY ______________

17 LARK ______________ **18** PLAN ______________

Decode these words using the same code as above.

19 elug ______________ **20** iohz ______________

Total

Time for a break! Go to Puzzle Page 42

Test time: 0   5   10 minutes

Complete the following sentences in the best way by choosing one word from each set of brackets.

Example Tall is to (tree, <u>short</u>, colour) as narrow is to (thin, white, <u>wide</u>).

1 Ostrich is to (egg, bird, Africa) as fly is to (insect, sky, soar).

2 Speak is to (talk, mouth, word) as pace is to (stripe, stride, stand).

3 Hilarious is to (miserable, funny, comforting) as tragic is to (alive, fantastic, sad).

A B C D E F G H I J K L M N O P Q R S T U V W X Y Z

Fill in the missing letters and numbers. The alphabet has been written out to help you.

Example AB is to CD as PQ is to ___RS___ .

4 PON is to MLK as JIH is to _____.

5 FD is to HF as JH is to _____.

6 Ah is to Dk as Gn is to _____.

7 Z11 is to X10 as V9 is to _____.

8 M12N is to O14p as Q16R is to _____.

9 aZ is to bY as cX is to _____.

10 AF is to CH as EJ is to _____.

A B C D E F G H I J K L M N O P Q R S T U V W X Y Z

Give the two missing groups of letters and numbers in the following sequences. The alphabet has been written out to help you.

Example	CQ	DP	EQ	FP	<u>GQ</u>	<u>HP</u>		
11	10	4	20	6	___	___		
12	Ab	Cd	Ef	Gh	___	___		
13	33	zz	22	yy	___	___		
14	15m	18p	21s	24v	___	___		
15	___	___	8	16	32	64		
16	6	___	12	8	___	12	24	16
17	___	2	4	___	6	8	8	16
18	a3Z	b5Y	___	___	e11V	f13U	g15T	h17S
19	___	___	16	15	20	18	24	21
20	3Z	___	6X	___	13V	18U	24T	31S

(11)

Total

Look at these groups of words.

A	B	C	D	E
rugby	iron	eagle	scarlet	rain
netball	lead	penguin	orange	cloud

Choose the correct group for each of these words below. Write in the group letter.

1–5   steel   _____   flamingo   _____   hail   _____

      purple   _____   azure   _____   hockey   _____

      sun   _____   seagull   _____   platinum   _____

      football   _____

Find two letters that will end the first word and start the second word.

Example   pas (_t_ _a_) ste

   6   cla (__ __) oon   **7**   swiv (__ __) ect

   8   sty (__ __) mon   **9**   varni (__ __) out

  10   pan (__ __) icle

Remove one letter from the word in capital letters to leave a new word.
The meaning of the new word is given in the clue.

Example   AUNT   an insect   _ANT_

11   TABLE   a story   _____

12   CLIMB   an arm or a leg   _____

13   BRIDLE   marries a groom   _____

14   FOWL   a night bird   _____

15   STEEP   a pace   _____

Underline the two words that are the odd ones out in the following groups of words.

Example   black   <u>king</u>   purple   green   <u>house</u>

16   boot   door   slipper   car   snowshoe

17   beetroot   carrot   peach   apple   clementine

18   bear   camel   salmon   crocodile   mouse

19   camera   CD player   radio   tape recorder   binoculars

20   forest   lake   orchard   pond   wood

Total

Underline the two words, one from each group, that are the closest in meaning.

Example (race, shop, <u>start</u>)   (finish, <u>begin</u>, end)

1   (appear, disappear, collapse)   (vanish, rebuild, apply)

2   (competent, competitor, companion)   (capable, enemy, canopy)

3   (blue, aquamarine, scarlet)   (black, beige, crimson)

4   (scamper, run, skip)   (hop, scurry, scrounge)

5   (rubbish, wasteful, skip)   (dust, wasteland, uneconomical)

Write the four-letter word hidden at the end of one word and the beginning of the next word. The order of the letters may not be changed.

Example We had bat<u>s and</u> balls.   _sand_

6   Please remember you must open each window slowly.   _____

7   I avoided the girl who made me cry.   _____

8   The rope bridge swung in the breeze.   _____

9   Explorers make epic journeys across the globe.   _____

10   Tom's ball dented the wing of his father's car.   _____

From the information supplied, underline the one statement below it that must be true.

11   Butter is a dairy product. Dairy products are made from milk.

   A Butter is made from milk.   **C** Dairy products are yellow.

   B Milk comes from cows.   **D** Cheese is a dairy product.

Find the letter which will end the first word and start the second word.

Example peac (_h_) ome

12   buil (___) rown   13   stam (___) roud

14   twic (___) ndure   15   dais (___) earn

If A = 5, S = 4, T = 3, R = 2 and E = 1, find the values of the following words when the letters are added together.

16   RAT   _____   17   EAR   _____

18   STAR   _____   19   REST   _____

20   STARE   _____

Total

TEST 13: **Mixed**

Test time: 0 |||||5|||||10 minutes

Here are the number codes for four words.
3256   3526   6225   5223
Match the right code to each word.

1   FROM   _____   **2**   ROOF   _____

3   FORM   _____   **4**   MOOR   _____

5   Using the same code, decode 5226   _____

Write the four-letter word hidden at the end of one word and the beginning of the next word. The order of the letters may not be changed.

Example   We had bat<u>s and</u> balls.   _____*sand*_____

6   I was stung by a wasp in my garden.   _____

7   In the dusk the nightingales were singing.   _____

8   The team stays in cheap hotels to save money.   _____

9   The tide tugged at the tarred rope holding the anchor.   _____

10   Ben and his friends consumed three loaves of bread.   _____

Find a word that is similar in meaning to the word in capital letters and that rhymes with the second word.

Example   CABLE   tyre   _____*wire*_____

11   DIVIDE   hair   _____

12   TALK   flat   _____

13   LABOUR   spoil   _____

14   ASCEND   rhyme   _____

15   SOIL   mirth   _____

Change the first word into the last word by changing one letter at a time, and making two new, different words in the middle.

Example   CASE   _____*CASH*_____   _____*WASH*_____   WISH

16   FLIT   _____   _____   PLAN

17   BUSY   _____   _____   BELT

18   PART   _____   _____   CORD

19   COIN   _____   _____   BARN

20   FLEX   _____   _____   BREW

(14)

Total

Rearrange the muddled words in capital letters in the following sentences so that they make sense.

Example There are sixty SNODCES _seconds_ in a UTMINE _minute_ .

1   RAHSSK _____ are fierce predators that WDLEL _____ in the sea.

2   Half of VYSNTEE _____ is YRTHTI _____ five.

3   Myles prefers to play GBRYU _____ rather than BLFOOALT _____ .

4   There are many SHMLSEEO _____ people on the London TSERETS _____ .

5   The ISOTRHC _____ is the GELARTS _____ flightless bird.

Underline two words, one from each group, that go together to form a new word. The word in the first group always comes first.

Example (hand, <u>green</u>, for)   (light, <u>house</u>, sure)

6   (kind, hard, for)   (beds, nurses, wards)   **7**   (crack, break, mend) (slow, fast, full)

8   (grand, after, before) (day, noon, hour)   **9**   (pick, ball, match)   (stick, nick, miss)

10   (water, free, tide)   (sun, fall, wave)

Find and underline the two words that need to change places for each sentence to make sense.

Example She went to <u>letter</u> the <u>write</u>.

11   Please close the quietly door.

12   Marion more one mark got than Jason.

13   In the snow the dark was falling softly.

14   Her shirt birthday present was the favourite.

15   He likes to play Saturdays on football.

BROTH   BROAD   BROOM   BROKE   BROOK

If these words were written in alphabetical order which word would be:

16   first?   _____   17   last?   _____

Fill in the crossword so that all the words are included.

18–20   RARER   SUGAR
          SIDES   SAFER
          DRIER   FLING

Total

TEST 15: **Mixed**

Complete the following sentences by selecting the most sensible word from each group of words given in the brackets. Underline the words selected.

Example The (<u>children</u>, boxes, foxes) carried the (houses, <u>books</u>, steps) home from the (greengrocer, <u>library</u>, factory).

1 The footballer (picked, kicked, licked) the (ice cream, apple, ball) into the (back, stomach, heart) of the net.

2 The business (deal, class, man) took his (newspaper, sandwiches, desk) out of his briefcase and began to (read, eat, write) it.

3 (Why, Who, How) can I help you with your homework if (he, she, you) haven't brought your (books, cushions, hats) home?

4 At midday the grandfather (clock, man, chair) in our hallway (chimes, jumps, talks) (two, eight, twelve) times.

5 In order to (sleep, climb, write) neatly you will need to (eat, sharpen, break) your (pencil, knife, rubber).

Underline the one word in each group that **cannot be made** from the letters of the word in capital letters.

Example STATIONERY   stone   tyres   ration   <u>nation</u>   noisy

6	ELASTIC	stile	scale	steal	stick	slice
7	GRAPEFRUIT	pager	treat	tiger	grate	purge
8	SPLENDOUR	round	proud	unless	loner	drops
9	STRAIGHT	shirt	right	thirst	stride	tights
10	PLEASANT	least	stale	plane	nasal	please

The code for the word BRIGHTER is 56174236. Encode each of these words using the same code.

11 GRIT _____   **12** TRIBE _____

Decode these codes using the same code as above.

13 4365 _____   **14** 431742 _____   **15** 21736 _____

Give the two missing numbers in each sequence.

Example   CQ   DP   EQ   FP   <u>GQ</u>   <u>HP</u>

16 38   35   ___   29   ___   23   **17** 17   20   24   29   ___   ___

18 2   4   ___   16   32   ___   **19** 5   16   6   18   ___   ___   8   22

20 ___   17   44   ___   33   21   22   23

Total

Fill in the crosswords so that all the words are included.

1–3

CHAIR   RADAR

MOTOR   CHASM

AWARD   AWAIT

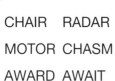

4–6

MEETS   SHEDS

SOCKS   OLIVE

CRIME   STORM

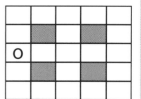

From the information supplied, underline the one statement below it that must be true.

7   My dustbin is black. My rubbish collection is on Thursdays.

    A   All black dustbins are emptied on Thursdays.

    B   My dustbin is emptied on Thursdays.

    C   Thursday is a convenient day for rubbish collection.

    D   My black dustbin is rubbish.

A B C D E F G H I J K L M N O P Q R S T U V W X Y Z

The word FLOWER is written in code as GMPXFS. Encode each of these words using the same code.

8   ROW   _____   **9**   LEAF   _____

10   Decode TVOOZ using the same code.   _____

Move one letter from the first word to the second word to make two new words.

Example   hunt   sip   _hut_   _snip_

11   spear   teak   _____   _____

12   mange   hue   _____   _____

13   frail   stay   _____   _____

14   broom   led   _____   _____

15   tired   tout   _____   _____

Write the four-letter word hidden at the end of one word and the beginning of the next word. The order of the letters may not be changed.

Example   We had bat<u>s and</u> balls.   _sand_

16   It was remarkable how fast army tanks appeared.   _____

17   The Australians batted until eleven o'clock.   _____

18   Watch out, there is a hair on that piece of cake!   _____

19   I wish chocolate fountains would flow all the time.   _____

20   I catch the school bus to my village every day.   _____

Time for a break! Go to Puzzle Page 43 ▶   Total

Look at these words. Sort them into groups.

1–4 Ford   metre   Berlin   pineapple
         Venice   Vauxhall   banana   millimetre

A	B	C	D
Cars	Measurements	Cities	Fruit
_____	_____	_____	_____
_____	_____	_____	_____

Add one letter to the word in capital letters to make a new word. The meaning of the new word is given in the clue.

Example PLAN   simple   PLAIN

5   CEASE   a fold in material   _____

6   PLATE   the roof of your mouth   _____

7   READ   not look forward to   _____

8   TAPER   to interfere with   _____

Underline the two words that are the odd ones out in the following groups of words.

Example black <u>king</u> purple green <u>house</u>

9   ring   circle necklace bracelet box   **10** breakfast lunch cup   plate   dinner

11 finger nail   tack   screw   shoe   **12** bite   tooth chew munch lip

Rearrange the letters in capitals to make another word. The new word has something to do with the first two words or phrases.

Example spot   soil   SAINT   STAIN

13 brown   breakfast bread   STOAT   _____

14 mouldy   not fresh   LEAST   _____

15 surplus   an extra one   REAPS   _____

16 wall covering covers a wound   STAPLER   _____

Complete the following sentences in the best way by choosing one word from each set of brackets.

Example Tall is to (tree, <u>short</u>, colour) as narrow is to (thin, white, <u>wide</u>).

17   King is to (crown, queen, kingdom) as judge is to (wig, jury, bench).

18   Fish is to (cod, scales, chips) as bird is to (beak, wing, feathers).

19   Deer is to (antlers, venison, fawn) as cow is to (steak, beef, milk).

20   Hammer is to (tool, nail, anvil) as spanner is to (screw, pin, nut).

Total

Underline one word in brackets that will go equally well with both the pairs of words outside the brackets.

Example rush, attack   cost, fee   (price, hasten, strike, <u>charge</u>, money)

1	examine, inspect	stop, limit	(test, check, restrain, study)
2	correctly, properly	brim, rise	(right, well, simply, spring)
3	imitate, mirror	think, consider	(reflect, demonstrate, ponder, return)
4	boundary, edge	confine, curb	(margin, pavement, limit, restrict)
5	affordable, inexpensive	second-rate, inferior	(mean, reasonable, low, cheap)

A B C D E F G H I J K L M N O P Q R S T U V W X Y Z

Fill in the missing letters. The alphabet has been written out to help you.

Example AB is to CD as PQ is to ___RS___ .

6   ACF is to GIL as MOR is to _____.   **7**   ZX is to WU as TR is to _____.

8   ZA is to XC as VE is to _____.   **9**   ZW is to TQ as NK is to _____.

10 AmD is to GnJ as MoP is to _____.

In her basket, Amy had beans, carrots, cucumber, mushrooms and tomatoes. Work out which section of the supermarket shelves she found her items on.

11–15

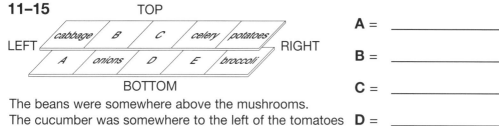

A = _____

B = _____

C = _____

D = _____

E = _____

The beans were somewhere above the mushrooms.
The cucumber was somewhere to the left of the tomatoes but not under the carrots.
The carrots, in turn, were directly above the mushrooms.

Look at the first group of three words. The word in the middle has been made from the two other words. Complete the second group of three words in the same way, making a new word in the middle of the group.

Example PAI<u>N</u> INTO <u>TO</u>OK   ALSO   _SOON_   ONLY

16	SLAP	LACK	DOCK	PICK	_____	HEED
17	SORT	STOP	OPEN	FEEL	_____	OXEN
18	POOL	LOVE	SAVE	SEAL	_____	LIMB
19	MASH	SALE	TEAL	WAGE	_____	PERT
20	FLAG	GLAD	DRAB	SLIP	_____	GRUB

19

Total

Underline the two words, one from each group, which are the most opposite in meaning.

Example (dawn, <u>early</u>, wake)   (<u>late</u>, stop, sunrise)

1   (off, under, up)   (on, through, by)

2   (steaming, warm, icy)   (cool, sleet, cold)

3   (for, again, by)   (up, through, against)

4   (leave, grant, give)   (pull, apply, take)

5   (point, sharp, apex)   (notice, blunt, hill)

A B C D E F G H I J K L M N O P Q R S T U V W X Y Z

Give the two missing groups of letters in the following sequences. The alphabet has been written out to help you.

Example CQ   DP   EQ   FP   <u>GQ</u>   <u>HP</u>

6   AC   EG   IK   MO   QS   _____   _____

7   ZP   YQ   XR   WS   VT   _____   _____

8   CAD   DBE   ECF   FDG   GEH   _____   _____

9   AZ   CX   EV   GT   IR   _____   _____

10   feg   gfh   hgi   ihj   jik   _____   _____

Find the letter which will end the first word and start the second word.

Example peac (_h_) ome

11   clea (___) eign   12   spac (___) njoy

13   tric (___) icks   14   rel (___) ell

15   tune (___) esk

Here are the number codes for four words.
9413 9471 7413 9331
Match the right code to each word.

16   LACK   _____   17   LAKE   _____

18   LEEK   _____   19   CAKE   _____

Decode this word using the same code as above.

20   1493   _____

Total

Test 20: **Mixed**

Write the four-letter word hidden at the end of one word and the beginning of the next word. The order of the letters may not be changed.

Example We had ba<u>ts an</u>d balls.   _sand_

1   We saw nothing but desert stretching before us.   _____

2   Mrs Smith knelt down to dust under the table.   _____

3   Neither the zebra nor the antelope heard the lion.   _____

4   The pies are in the oven.   _____

5   Some people think taking vitamins helps stop illnesses spreading. _____

From the information supplied, underline the one statement below it that must be true.

6   French is taught at our school. Our class has a French lesson on Friday.

   A All schools teach French.   **C** French is taught only on Friday.

   B We have a French lesson on Friday. **D** Our school is in France.

The code for the word CLOTHES is written as @!+?/*£. Decode these words using the same code as above.

7   @+£?   _____   8   £@/++!   _____   9   @/**£*   _____

Encode these words using the same code as above.

10   HOTEL   _____   11   THOSE   _____

Complete the following sentences in the best way by choosing one word from each set of brackets.

Example Tall is to (tree, <u>short</u>, colour) as narrow is to (thin, white, <u>wide</u>).

12   Pen is to (paper, write, biro) as brush is to (paint, blue, easel).

13   Water is to bottle as (milk, petrol, meat) is to (mouth, garage, carton).

14   (Trousers, Top, Under) is to bottom as high is to (above, over, low).

15   Mind is to (think, read, care) as stomach is to (digest, fat, ache).

16   Go is to (get, come, stop) as green is to (amber, red, light).

If a = 5, b = 4, c = 3, d = 2 and e = 1, find the value of the following.

17   $(a + b) - (c + d) =$ _____   18 $\dfrac{bc}{d} =$ _____

19   $(d^2 + c^2) - e =$ _____   20 $\dfrac{be}{d} + a =$ _____

Total [   ]

TEST 21: **Mixed**

Find a word that is similar in meaning to the word in capital letters and that rhymes with the second word.

Example CABLE   tyre   _wire_

1	ENCLOSURE	dense	_____	**2**	LIQUID	course	_____
3	CONFUSE	cuddle	_____	**4**	SHARE	mice	_____

Find a word that can be put in front of each of the following words to make a new, compound word.

Example cast   fall   word   pour   _down_

5	fall	mark	proof	colour	_____
6	fighter	work	side	arm	_____
7	man	drop	ball	flake	_____
8	forest	drop	coat	bow	_____

If these words are placed in alphabetical order, which comes fourth?

9	flatworm	flatbed	fledgling	flannel	flank	_____
10	stagnant	stagecoach	stagger	stadium	stainless	_____
11	harness	harmonic	harelip	harpoon	harrier	_____
12	larder	larva	larceny	lapwing	largesse	_____

Find the three-letter word that can be added to the letters in capitals to make a new word. The new word will complete the sentence sensibly. Write the three-letter word.

Example The cat sprang onto the MO.   _USE_

13	Our car has new tyres on each WH.	_____
14	The headmaster said my H was too long and needed cutting.	_____
15	There are not enough chairs so he is STING.	_____
16	CRIES are a red fruit with a stone in the middle.	_____

A B C D E F G H I J K L M N O P Q R S T U V W X Y Z

Give the two missing pairs of letters in the following sequences. The alphabet has been written out to help you.

Example CQ DP EQ FP _GQ_ _HP_

17	AX	DU	GR	JO	ML	___ ___	**18**	WV	YX	AZ	CB	ED	___ ___
19	GQ	HQ	IR	JR	KS	___ ___	**20**	BW	BV	CU	CT	DS	___ ___

22

Total

Underline the pair of words most opposite in meaning.

Example cup, mug   coffee, milk   <u>hot, cold</u>

1   win, lose   win, success   failure, disappointment

2   hot, cool   warm, cool   cold, warm

3   clear, lucid   cloudy, rainy   clear, cloudy

4   stand, deliver   collect, deliver   send, deliver

Find the missing number by using the two numbers outside the brackets in the same way as the other sets of numbers.

Example   2 [8] 4   3 [18] 6   5 [<u>25</u>] 5

5   7 [10] 1   3 [18] 5   4 [___] 2

6   14 [11] 4   13 [7] 7   12 [___] 3

7   5 [15] 2   7 [5] 6   4 [___] 3

8   6 [8] 7   7 [6] 4   8 [___] 3

Underline the word the brackets which goes best with the words given outside the brackets.

Example word, paragraph, sentence   (pen, cap, <u>letter</u>, top, stop)

9   rush, dash, shoot   (arrow, dart, rifle, move, jog)

10   honest, light, just   (true, pale, dark, fair, time)

11   remove, expel, emit   (take, school, bully, reject, eject)

12   rotund, portly, heavy   (weight, harbour, stout, stone, round)

Move one letter from the first word to the second word to make two new words.

Example hunt   sip   ___hut___   ___snip___

13   crane   bed   _____ _____   **14**   plight   car   _____ _____

15   suet   urn   _____ _____   **16**   flood   hit   _____ _____

Underline the two words that are made from the same letters.

Example TAP   PET   <u>TEA</u>   POT   <u>EAT</u>

17   SHEARS   SHEEP   SHAPES   PHASES   SHORTS

18   STRONG   GRUNTS   GRANTS   STRAIN   STRUNG

19   STAPLE   PLEASE   PALEST   APPLES   SCRAPE

20   BLAST   STOLE   STALE   LABEL   LEAST

Total

Look at these groups of words.

A	B	C	D	E
pencil	oak	seaside	table	trout
ruler	elm	sandcastle	cupboard	carp

Choose the correct group for each of these words below. Write in the group letter.

1–5 beech _____   rubber _____   perch _____   pike _____   beach _____

bed _____   pen _____   pine _____   chair _____   seaweed _____

Remove one letter from the word in capital letters to leave a new word.
The meaning of the new word is given in the clue.

Example AUNT   an insect   ___ANT___

6	FRAME	well known	_____
7	CHEAT	to make hotter	_____
8	PLANT	organise	_____
9	CRATER	supply	_____
10	LADDER	snake	_____

Underline the word in the brackets that is most opposite in meaning to the word in capitals.

Example WIDE   (broad, vague, long, <u>narrow</u>, motorway)

11 THIN   (thick, healthy, full, emaciated, skinny)

12 EASY   (simple, facile, difficult, descriptive, quick)

13 FULL   (avoid, replete, refill, empty, complete)

14 FLAT   (level, uneven, square, apartment, deflated)

15 QUIET   (noisy, quite, crowded, whispering, tranquil)

Underline the pair of words most similar in meaning.

Example come, go   <u>roams, wanders</u>   fear, fare

16	high, low	climb, ascend	lift, descend
17	polite, impolite	before, now	concur, agree
18	healthy, well	well, lake	health, happiness
19	dart, dodge	dodge, budge	arrow, dart
20	pillow, bed	carpet, rug	bucket, spade

Total

TEST 1: Similars and Opposites (page 2)

1 **tidy, scruffy** 'Tidy' means neat whereas 'scruffy' means untidy.
2 **broad, narrow** 'Broad' means wide whereas 'narrow' means thin.
3 **unwell, healthy** 'Unwell' means ill whereas 'healthy' means well.
4 **pale, flushed** A 'pale' face looks very white whereas a 'flushed' face is reddened.
5 **protect**   6 **piece**
7 **tie**   8 **tiny**
9 **few, many**   10 **stupid, sensible**
11 **present, absent** 12 **far, near**
13 **silence** The closest in meaning to 'QUIET' is 'silence' because they both mean the absence of noise.
14 **group** The closest in meaning to 'CLASS' is 'group' as both mean a collection or gathering of people.
15 **shred** The closest in meaning to 'TEAR' is 'shred' as they both mean to rip up into pieces.
16 **question** The closest in meaning to 'QUERY' is 'question' as they both mean to ask, request or enquire.
17 **laugh** To 'cry' can be a result of being 'upset'. The result of 'happy' can be to 'laugh'.
18 **against** 'Left' and 'right' are antonyms in the same way 'for' and 'against' are the opposite of each other.
19 **ankle** A 'finger' is part of a hand attached to a 'wrist'. A 'toe' is part of a foot attached to an 'ankle'.
20 **keep** 'Reveal' and 'show' are synonyms, as are 'retain' and 'keep'.

TEST 2: Sorting Words (page 3)

1 **claw** A 'claw' can be like a nail or hook and, as a verb, mean to scrape or graze.
2 **level** 'Level' can mean smooth and also a rank or height of something.
3 **tip** 'Tip' means to let fall; it also means the top of something like the apex of a mountain.
4 **place** 'Place' is the whereabouts of something or how you use or employ something.
5 **pure** 'Pure' is fresh and unsullied and, particularly if applied to a person, means natural and genuine.
6 **basket, kitchen**   7 **outside, jacket**
8 **English, lesson**   9 **library, varied**
10 **school, camping**   11 **THORN**
12 **CLASP**   13 **BLEAT**
14 **THROB**   15 **DENIM**
16 The **toilet** sign has fallen off the **door**.
17 You have arrived **just** in **time** for tea.

18 Why have you put your **shoes** on the wrong **feet**?
19 In a **storm**, the **park** bench was blown over.
20 The **leaves** fall during **autumn**.

TEST 3: Selecting Words (page 4)

1 **r** rage, rally, rat, roar, reach
2 **v** vice, van, valley, vomit, vow
3 **c** chunk, clash, chip, crush, craft
4 **m** mash, malign, mutter, meat, mail
5 **id** squid, idea
6 **re** spare, really
7 **st** twist, stop
8 **th** both, thorn
9 **troublesome**
10 **invest**   11 **begun**   12 **endless**
13 **lane** A 'lane' is a thoroughfare in the same way as a 'road', a 'street' and an 'avenue'.
14 **foot** 'Toes', 'ankle' and 'heel' are all parts of the 'foot'.
15 **pen** All the words are items of stationery.
16 **trainer** All the words are items of footwear or shoes.
17 **crate**   18 **stone**
19 **slope**   20 **folder**

TEST 4: Finding Words (page 5)

1 **leap** A long icic**le ap**peared on her windowsill last night.
2 **howl** he ghostly sound of bot**h owl**s could be heard
3 **vest** My cousins ha**ve st**ones all around their pond.
4 **cell** In an airport lounge any unattended par**cel l**ooks suspicious.
5 **mint** Pour the crea**m int**o the striped jug please.
6 **ATE** water
7 **ILL** village
8 **SIN** crossing
9 **YES** eyes
10 **PEA** speaking
11 **super** supermarket, supermodel, supernatural, superstar
12 **some** something, somehow, somewhat, somebody
13 **eye** eyewitness, eyeshadow, eyebrow, eyeball
14 **rain** raindrop, raincoat, rainforest, rainbow
15 **life** lifeguard, lifeboat, lifestyle, lifetime
16 **a** bred, taint
17 **g** bun, gamble
18 **t** wan, pint
19 **l** bride, growling
20 **h** wine, hearth

EXPANDED ANSWERS

Bond Verbal Reasoning 10 Minute Tests 10–11+ years

A1

TEST 5: Alphabetical Order and Substitution (page 6)

1–5 Use grids to help you.

1 circle

c	a	l	l	e	d		1st
c	h	a	r	g	e		2nd
c	i	r	c	l	e		3rd
c	o	l	o	u	r		4th
c	u	r	r	i	e	s	5th

2 quaver

q	u	a	r	r	y	1st
q	u	a	r	t	z	2nd
q	u	a	v	e	r	3rd
q	u	e	e	n		4th
q	u	i	l	t	s	5th

3 drench

d	r	a	g	o	n	1st
d	r	e	a	m	s	2nd
d	r	e	n	c	h	3rd
d	r	i	n	k	s	4th
d	r	o	w	s	y	5th

4 pillow

p	a	l	a	c	e	1st
p	a	n	d	a	s	2nd
p	i	l	l	o	w	3rd
p	l	a	c	e	d	4th
p	l	a	n	e	t	5th

5 galaxy

g	a	b	l	e	s	1st
g	a	i	n	e	d	2nd
g	a	l	a	x	y	3rd
g	a	l	l	o	p	4th
g	a	r	d	e	n	5th

6 **7** $(10 + 3) - 6 = 7$ 7 **60** $10 \times 6 = 60$

8 **36** $(24 \div 4) \times 6 = 36$

9 **16** $(24 - 10) + (6 - 4) = 16$

10 **p** $(24 - 4) - 10 = 10$ $10 = p$

11 **u** $4 \times 3 \times 2 = 24$ $24 = u$

12 **u** $(10 \times 3) - 6 = 24$ $24 = u$

13 **s** $(4 \times 4) - 10 = 6$ $6 = s$

14 **r** $(4 \times 6) \div 24 + 2 = 3$ $3 = r$

15 **r** $(6 + 24) \div 10 = 3$ $3 = r$

16 **17** $4 + 3 + 2 + 1 + 5 + 2 = 17$

17 **16** $4 + 3 + 2 + 1 + 6 = 16$

18 **17** $3 + 2 + 1 + 5 + 6 = 17$

19 **21** $5 + 6 + 1 + 4 + 3 + 2 = 21$

20 **5** Take the letters 'PALE' out of 'LAPSE', it leaves 'S' which equals 5.

TEST 6: Word Progressions (page 7)

1–4 Use grids as shown below to help work out the missing word.

1 PLAN

1	2	3*			4	3*		
G	R	I	N		P	I	N	K

1	2	3*			4	3*		
P	L	U	G		N	A	V	E

2 ELSE

	2	1			3			4
T	I	M	E		L	O	O	K

	2	1			3			4
S	L	E	D		S	O	R	E

3 TRAY

2		1	4*		4*	3		
P	A	S	T		T	O	R	N

2		1	4*		4*	3		
R	O	T	A		Y	A	W	N

4 NAVE

	2		1/4*		3		1/4*	
D	U	M	B		L	O	B	E

	2		1/4*		3		1/4*	
L	A	W	N		V	E	E	R

5 **LOOM, LOOK**   6 **CUBE, CURE**

7 **BOAT, BEAT**   8 **FORT, FORM**

9 **DIRT, DART**   10 **TAME, SAME**

11 **sole** The 'age' of the first word in each pair changes to 'ole' in the second word.

12 **bout** The 'ea' of the first word in each pair changes to 'ou' in the second word.

13 **isle** The first and last letters of the first words are removed in the second word.

14 **toll** The first and third letters of the first word are removed in the second word.

15–20 Solve these questions by looking at the first set of three and working out how the first and last numbers have been used to arrive at the middle number. Apply this to the second set of three and see if it works. If it does, apply it to the last set.

15 **45** $7 \times 4 = 28$ and $6 \times 3 = 18$, so $9 \times 5 = 45$

16 **24** $(4 + 1) \times 2 = 10$ and $(3 + 6) \times 2 = 18$, so $(5 + 7) \times 2 = 24$

17 3 7 ÷ 7 = 1 and 6 ÷ 3 = 2, so 12 ÷ 4 = 3
18 2 (5 × 4) − 10 = 10 and (3 × 8) − 10 = 14, so (2 × 6) − 10 = 2
19 17 4 + 3 = 7 and 9 + 8 = 17, so 11 + 6 = 17
20 1 (6 × 2) − 2 = 10 and (5 × 3) − 3 = 12, so (2 × 1) − 1 = 1

TEST 7: Logic (page 8)

1–6 From the information you know that History is opposite Geography, so they must be in both Room 3 and Room 8 as no other rooms are directly opposite each other. In the last sentence you learn that Maths is next door to both Geography and Science. Only three rooms are directly next door to each other. So, Science 5, Maths 4, Geography 3 and therefore, History 8. This leaves English and French. The first sentence states that English has a lower number than French, so English 1 and French 7.

1 Room 1: English
2 Room 3: Geography
3 Room 4: Maths
4 Room 5: Science
5 Room 7: French
6 Room 8: History

7–11 Use the compass points and a grid to help you.

CAMP	MOUNTAINS	
JUNGLE	SWAMP	
		EXPLORER

7 jungle   **8 mountains**   **9 north**
10 west   **11 north-west**

12–20 A table is the easiest way to sort the information, like this:

	Rabbits	Goldfish	Cat	Dog	Gerbil	Tortoise
Darren	✓			✓		
William	✓			✓	✓	
Sita	✓	✓	✓			✓
Jane	✓	✓	✓			
Phil	✓					✓
Brett		✓	✓		✓	
Sven		✓	✗			
Sandy					✓	

12 6
15 8
18 William
13–14 rabbit and dog
16–17 Sandy and Sven
19 Brett   **20 Sita**

TEST 8: Simple Codes (page 9)

1 1946 T = 1, R = 9, U = 4, E = 6
2 9438 R = 9, U = 4, M = 3, P = 8
3 MORE 3 = M, 2 = O, 9 = R, 6 = E
4 PORT 8 = P, 2 = O, 9 = R, 1 = T
5 NEST A = N, J = E, O = S, Z = T
6 STEP O = S, Z = T, J = E, R = P
7 £ + x − M = £, A = +, L = x, E = −
8 @ + $ − R = @, A = +, C = $, E = −
9–13 Two words begin with 'T' so T = 4. Two words end 'ST' so S = 3 and T = 4. Knowing these number and letter pairings will allow you to work out the rest.
9 TAME 4 = T, 6 = A, 1 = M, 7 = E
10 TEST 4 = T, 7 = E, 3 = S, 4 = T
11 STEM 3 = S, 4 = T, 7 = E, 1 = M
12 MAST 1 = M, 6 = A, 3 = S, 4 = T
13 EAST 7 = E, 6 = A, 3 = S, 4 = T
14 MEAT 1 = M, 7 = E, 6 = A, 4 = T
15–20 Two of the codes end 'm 9', so m = T and 9 = S. The code beginning '9 m' therefore is 'STAR'. Knowing these number and letter pairings will allow you to work out the rest.
15 m X % 3 T = m, U = X, R = %, N = 3
16 % Q m 9 R = %, A = Q, T = m, S = 9
17 9 m Q % S = 9, T = m, A = Q, R = %
18 3 X m 9 N = 3, U = X, T = m, S = 9
19 9 m X 3 m S = 9, T = m, U = X, N = 3, T = m
20 9 Q m X % 3 S = 9, A = Q, T = m, U = X, R = %, N = 3

TEST 9: More Complicated Codes (page 10)

1 TPDDFS To get from the word to the code, move each letter forwards one place.
2 GOAL To get from the code to the word, move each letter backwards one place.
3–4 To get from the word to the code, move each letter forwards two places.
3 LCO   **4 BGDTC**
5–6 To get from the word to the code, move each letter backwards three places.
5 QXYIB   **6 MFKH**
7–8 To get from the code to the word, move each letter forwards three places.
7 PART   **8 JADE**
9–13 Use a grid to help you.

A	B	C	D	E	F	G	H	I	J
1	2	3	4	5	6	7	8	9	10

EXPANDED ANSWERS

Bond Verbal Reasoning 10 Minute Tests 10–11+ years

9 **6554**   10 **3175**   11 **8514**
12 **FACE**   13 **HEDGE**
14 **QJKY** To get from the word to the code, move each letter forwards five places.
15–20 Use a grid to help you.

B	L	A	C	K
e	o	d	f	n

You know d = A and n = K. Two of the codes end 'dun'. Therefore, looking at the words, you can work out that u must be the code for R. So BARK = edun and LARK = odun. Two of the words begin with P so s = P. You can complete all the words and codes except the final letters represented by 'b' and 'q'. Therefore, go back to BLACK and the original code in the grid. Note the relationship between the letters and the code. To get from the word to the code, you move each letter forwards. To get from the code to the word, move backwards 3 places, so b = Y and q = N.

15 **edun** B = e, A = d, R = u, K = n
16 **sodb** P = s, L = o, A = d, Y = b
17 **odun** L = o, A = d, R = u, K = n
18 **sodq** P = s, L = o, A = d, N = q
19 **BIRD** e = B, I = I, u = R, g = D
20 **FLEW** i = F, o = L, h = E, z = W

TEST 10: Sequences (page 11)

1 **bird, insect** An 'ostrich' is a bird as a 'fly' is an 'insect'.
2 **talk, stride** To 'speak' means to converse or 'talk' as to 'pace' means to step or 'stride'.
3 **funny, sad** 'Hilarious' means extremely amusing or 'funny' as 'tragic' means extremely 'sad'.
4 **GFE** All three letters move backwards three places.
5 **LJ** Both letters move forwards two places.
6 **Jq** Both letters move forwards three places.
7 **T8** The letters move backwards two places. The numbers decrease by 1.
8 **S18t** Both letters move forward two places, and the second letter also changes from capitals (upper case) to lower case. The numbers in between them increase by 2.
9 **dW** The lower case letters are in alphabetical order. The capital letters are in reverse alphabetical order.
10 **GL** Both letters move forwards two places.
11 **30, 8** This is an alternating pattern. The first, third and fifth numbers increase by 10. The second, fourth and sixth numbers increase by 2.
12 **Ij, Kl** This is a consecutive pattern of the next alphabetical place. The first letter is in capitals, the second in lower case.

13 **11, xx** This is an alternating pattern. The numbers decrease by 11. The letters are in pairs and move backwards one place.
14 **27y, 30b** The numbers increase by 3. The letters move forward by three places. When you come to the end of the alphabet, wrap round to the beginning again: xyzabcC.
15 **2, 4** The numbers increase by doubling each time.
16 **4, 18** This is an alternating pattern. The first, third, fifth and seventh numbers increase by 6. The second, fourth, sixth and eighth numbers increase by 4.
17 **2, 4** This is an alternating pattern. The first, third, fifth and seventh numbers increase by 2. The second, fourth, sixth and eighth number is doubled each time.
18 **c7X, d9W** The lower case letter moves forward by one place. The number increases by 2. The capital letters move backwards one place.
19 **12, 12** This is an alternating pattern. The first, third, fifth and seventh numbers increase by 4. The second, fourth, sixth and eighth numbers increase by 3.
20 **4Y, 9W** The number added increases by 1 each time: +1, +2, +3, +4, +5, +6, +7. The letters are in reverse alphabetical order.

TEST 11: Mixed (page 12)

1–5 Category A is games (**hockey, football**). Category B is metals (**steel, platinum**). Category C is birds (**flamingo, seagull**). Category D is colours (**purple, azure**). Category E is weather types (**hail, sun**).
6 **sp** clasp, spoon
7 **el** swivel, elect
8 **le** style, lemon
9 **sh** varnish, shout
10 **ic** panic, icicle
11 **TALE**   12 **LIMB**   13 **BRIDE**
14 **OWL**   15 **STEP**
16 **door, car** The other words are all types of footwear.
17 **beetroot, carrot** The other words are all fruit.
18 **salmon, crocodile** The other words are all mammals.
19 **camera, binoculars** The other words you listen to.
20 **lake, pond** The other words all contain trees.

TEST 12: Mixed (page 13)

1 **disappear, vanish** Both the words mean to go from view, to become invisible.
2 **competent, capable** Both words mean experienced, skilled.

3 **scarlet, crimson** Both words are shades of red.
4 **scamper, scurry** Both words mean to dash or hurry.
5 **wasteful, uneconomical** Both words means extravagant, careless, inefficient.
6 **stop** Please remember you mu**st op**en each window slowly.
7 **whom** I avoided the girl **who m**ade me cry.
8 **hero** T**he ro**pe bridge swung in the breeze.
9 **keep** Explorers ma**ke ep**ic journeys across the globe.
10 **scar** Tom's ball dented the wing of his father'**s car**.
11 **A** You must use only the information given. B, C and D may or may not be true. They are not mentioned therefore you must reject them.
12 **d** build, drown
13 **p** stamp, proud
14 **e** twice, endure
15 **y** daisy, yearn
16 **10** $2 + 5 + 3 = 10$
17 **8** $1 + 5 + 2 = 8$
18 **14** $4 + 3 + 5 + 2 = 14$
19 **10** $2 + 1 + 4 + 3 = 10$
20 **15** $4 + 3 + 5 + 2 + 1 = 15$

TEST 13: Mixed (page 14)

1–5 Two of the codes have '22' in the middle. Therefore 2 = O. Two of the codes begin with '3'. Therefore, 3 = F. Knowing these letter and number pairings will allow you to work out the rest.
1 **3526** F = 3, R = 5, O = 2, M = 6
2 **5223** R = 5, O = 2, F = 3
3 **3256** F = 3, O = 2, R = 5, M = 6
4 **6225** M = 6, O = 2, R = 5
5 **ROOM** R = 5, O = 2, M = 6
6 **spin** I was stung by a wa**sp in** my garden.
7 **then** In the dusk **the n**ightingales were singing.
8 **inch** The team stays **in ch**eap hotels to save money.
9 **drop** The tide tugged at the tarre**d rop**e holding the anchor.
10 **reel** Ben and his friends consumed th**ree l**oaves of bread.
11 **share** 12 **chat**
13 **toil** 14 **climb**
15 **earth** 16 **FLAT, FLAN**
17 **BUST, BEST** 18 **CART, CARD**
19 **CORN, BORN** 20 **FLEW, BLEW**

TEST 14: Mixed (page 15)

1 **SHARKS, DWELL**
2 **SEVENTY, THIRTY**
3 **RUGBY, FOOTBALL**
4 **HOMELESS, LONDON**

5 **OSTRICH, LARGEST**
6 **forwards** 7 **breakfast** 8 **afternoon**
9 **matchstick** 10 **waterfall**
11 Please close the **door quietly**.
12 Marion **got** one mark **more** than Jason.
13 In the **dark** the **snow** was falling softly.
14 Her **favourite** birthday present was the **shirt**.
15 He likes to play **football** on **Saturdays**.
16–17 Arrange the words in a grid to make it easier to put them in the correct alphabetical order.

B	R	O	A	D		1ST
B	R	O	K	E		2ND
B	R	O	O	M		3RD
B	R	O	T	H		4TH

16 **BROAD** 17 **BROTH**
18–20

S	I	D	E	S
A		R		U
F	L	I	N	G
E		E		A
R	A	R	E	R

TEST 15: Mixed (page 16)

1–5 Try each of the words in the first set of brackets. Do they make sense with any words in the second and third set of brackets? Only one combination of three words makes sense.
1 **kicked, ball, back**
2 **man, newspaper, read**
3 **How, you, books**
4 **clock, chimes, twelve**
5 **write, sharpen, pencil**
6 **stick** There is no 'k' in ELASTIC'.
7 **treat** There is only one 'T' in GRAPEFRUIT'.
8 **unless** There is only one 'S' in SPLENDOUR'.
9 **stride** There is no 'E' and no 'D' in 'STRAIGHT'.
10 **please** There is only one 'E' in 'PLEASANT'.
11–15 Use a grid to help you.

B	R	I	G	H	T	E	R
5	6	1	7	4	2	3	6

11 **7612** G = 7, R = 6, I = 1, T = 2
12 **26153** T = 2, R = 6, I = 1, B = 5, E = 3
13 **HERB** 4 = H, 3 = E, 6 = R, 5 = B
14 **HEIGHT** 4 = H, 3 = E, 1 = I, 7 = G, 4 = H, 2 = T
15 **TIGER** 2 = T, 1 = I, 7 = G, 3 = E, 6 = R
16 **32, 26** Each number decreases by 3.
17 **35, 42** The number added increases by one each time: +3, +4, +5 +6 +7.
18 **8, 64** The number doubles each time, so $4 \times 2 = 8$ and $32 \times 2 = 64$.

Bond Verbal Reasoning 10 Minute Tests 10–11+ years

19 **7, 20** This is an alternating pattern. The first, third, fifth and seventh numbers increase by 1. The second, fourth, sixth and eighth numbers increase by 2.

20 **55, 19** This is an alternating pattern. The first, third, fifth and seventh numbers decrease by 11. The second, fourth, sixth and eighth numbers increase by 2.

TEST 16: Mixed (page 17)

1–3

C	H	A	S	M
H	■	W	■	O
A	W	A	I	T
I	■	R	■	O
R	A	D	A	R

4–6

S	O	C	K	S
T	■	R	■	H
O	L	I	V	E
R	■	M	■	D
M	E	E	T	S

7 **B** A, C and D may or may not be true. You must use only the information that is given.

8–10 To get from the word to the code, move the letters forwards one place.

8 **SPX** R = S, O = P, W = X

9 **MFBG** L = M, E = F, A = B, F = G

10 **SUNNY** To get from the code to the word, move the letters backwards one place. T = S, V = U, O = N, Z = Y

11 **s** pear, steak

12 **g** mane, huge

13 **r** fail, stray

14 **b** room, bled

15 **r** tied, trout

16 **star** It was remarkable how fa**st ar**my tanks appeared.

17 **tile** The Australians batted un**til e**leven o'clock.

18 **iron** Watch out, there is a ha**ir on** that piece of cake.

19 **wall** I wish chocolate fountains would flo**w all** the time.

20 **bust** I catch the school **bus t**o my village every day.

TEST 17: Mixed (page 18)

1–4 **A** Ford, Vauxhall
B metre, millimetre
C Berlin, Venice
D pineapple, banana

5 **CREASE**   6 **PALATE**
7 **DREAD**   8 **TAMPER**

9 **circle, box** The other words are items of jewellery.

10 **cup, plate** The other words are meals.

11 **finger, shoe** The other words are metal fixings.

12 **tooth, lip** The other words mean to gnaw or chomp.

13 **TOAST**   14 **STALE**
15 **SPARE**   16 **PLASTER**

17 **crown, wig** A 'king' wears a 'crown' as a 'judge' wears a 'wig'.

18 **scales, feathers** A 'fish' has 'scales' on its body in the same way a 'bird' has 'feathers'.

19 **venison, beef** 'venison' is 'deer' meat as 'beef' is 'cow' meat.

20 **nail, nut** A 'hammer' hits a 'nail' in place as a 'spanner' turns a 'nut'.

TEST 18: Mixed (page 19)

1 **check** 'Check' means to look at something carefully and also to restrain oneself.

2 **well** 'Well' means something done right and also to come to the brim, like tears in your eyes.

3 **reflect** To 'reflect' something is to show the image back again and also to ponder about a matter.

4 **limit** A 'limit' is the margin or perimeter; it also means to check or restrict something.

5 **cheap** A 'cheap' price is a low or reasonable one and 'cheap' can also mean low-grade or shoddy.

6 **SUX** Each letter moves forward six places.

7 **QO** Each letter moves backwards three places.

8 **TG** The first letter moves backwards two places. The second letter moves forward two places.

9 **HE** Each letter moves backwards six places.

10 **SpV** The capital letters (first and third letters) move forward six places. The lower case letter, in the middle, moves forward one place.

11–15 The final sentence in the information says the carrots are directly above the mushrooms. Therefore, the carrots must be C and the mushrooms D. The first sentence tells us the beans are on the top shelf, therefore B. If the cucumber is left of the tomatoes, they must be A, leaving the tomatoes in E.

A = cucumber
B = beans
C = carrots
D = mushrooms
E = tomatoes

Use grids as shown below to help work out the missing word.

16 ICED

	1	2	
S	L	A	P

		3	4
D	O	C	K

	1	2	
P	I	C	K

		3	4
H	E	E	D

17 FLEX

1	3*		2
S	O	R	T

3*	4		
O	P	E	N

1	3*		2
F	E	E	L

3*	4		
O	X	E	N

18 LAMB

	2*	2*	1
P	O	O	L

		3	4
S	A	V	E

	2*	2*	1
S	E	A	L

		3	4
L	I	M	B

19 GATE

	2*	1	
M	A	S	H

	4	2*	3
T	E	A	L

	2*	1	
W	A	G	E

	4	2*	3
P	E	R	T

20 PLUG

	2	3*	1
F	L	A	G

4		3*	
D	R	A	B

	2	3*	1
S	L	I	P

4		3*	
G	R	U	B

TEST 19: Mixed (page 20)

1 **off, on** Out of all the prepositions, these are the most opposite.
2 **warm, cool** 'Warm' is on the way to being hot in the way 'cool' is to cold, therefore they are the most opposite.
3 **for, against** 'For' is pro something and 'against' is anti or contrary to it.
4 **give, take** 'Give' is going away from you and 'take' is coming towards you.
5 **sharp, blunt** A 'sharp' pencil has a pointed end whereas a 'blunt' one is rounded and smooth.
6 **UW, YA** In each pair, the letters are moving forwards four places.
7 **UU, TV** The first letters are in reverse

alphabetical order. The second letters are in alphabetical order.
8 **HFI, IGJ** Each of the letters is in alphabetical order and moves forwards one place each time.
9 **KP, MN** The first letters move forwards two places. The second letters move backwards two letters.
10 **kjl, lkm** Each of the letters is in alphabetical order and moves forwards one place each time.
11 **r** clear, reign
12 **e** space, enjoy
13 **k** trick, kicks
14 **y** rely, yell
15 **d** tuned, desk
16–20 Three of the codes start with 9, so 9 = L. 3 = E as it is the only repeating number for the double E in LEEK. Knowing these number and letter pairings will allow you to work out the rest.
16 **9471** L = 9, A = 4, C = 7, K = 1
17 **9413** L = 9, A = 4, K = 1, E = 3
18 **9331** L = 9, E = 3, K = 1
19 **7413** C = 7, A = 4, K = 1, E = 3
20 **KALE** 1 = K, 4 = A, 9 = L, 3 = E

TEST 20: Mixed (page 21)

1 **sawn** We <u>saw n</u>othing but desert stretching before us.
2 **stun** Mrs Smith knelt down to du<u>st un</u>der the table.
3 **bran** Neither the ze<u>bra n</u>or the antelope heard the lion.
4 **rein** The pies <u>are in</u> the oven.
5 **pill** Some people think taking vitamins helps sto<u>p ill</u>nesses spreading.
6 **B** A, C and D may or may not be correct. However, they should be rejected as they are not referred to in the given information.
7–11 Use a grid to help you.

C	L	O	T	H	E	S
@	!	+	?	/	*	£

7 **COST** @ = C, + = O, £ = S, ? = T
8 **SCHOOL** £ = S, @ = C, / = H, + = O, + = O, ! = L
9 **CHEESE** @ = C, / = H, *= E, * = E, £ = S, * = E
10 **/ + ? * !** H = /, O = +, T = ?, E = *, L = !
11 **? / + £ *** T = ?, H = /, O = +, S = £, E = *
12 **write, paint** You 'write' with a 'pen' in the same way you 'paint' with a 'brush'.
13 **milk, carton** 'Water' often comes in a 'bottle' in the same way as 'milk' comes in a 'carton'.
14 **Top, low** 'Top' is an antonym of 'bottom' in the same way as 'high' is to 'low'.
15 **think, digest** A 'mind' 'thinks' in a similar way to a 'stomach' 'digests'.
16 **stop, red** 'Go' is an antonym of 'stop' in the same

EXPANDED ANSWERS

Bond Verbal Reasoning 10 Minute Tests 10–11+ years

way as a 'green' traffic light is to a 'red' one.

17 **4** $(5 + 4) - (3 + 2) = 4$
18 **6** $(4 \times 3) \div 2 = 6$
19 **12** $(2 \times 2) + (3 \times 3) - 1 = 12$
20 **7** $(4 \times 1) \div 2 + 5 = 7$

TEST 21: Mixed (page 22)

1 **fence**   2 **sauce**
3 **muddle**   4 **slice**
5 **water** waterfall, watermark, waterproof, watercolour
6 **fire** firefighter, firework, fireside, firearm
7 **snow** snowman, snowdrop, snowball, snowflake
8 **rain** rainforest, raindrop, raincoat, rainbow
9–12 Arrange the words in a gird to make it easier to put them in the correct alphabetical order.
9 **flatworm**

f	l	a	n	k				1st
f	l	a	n	n	e	l		2nd
f	l	a	t	b	e	d		3rd
f	l	a	t	w	o	r	m	4th
f	l	e	d	g	l	i	n	g	5th

10 **stagnant**

s	t	a	d	i	u	m			1st
s	t	a	g	e	c	o	a	c	h	2nd
s	t	a	g	g	e	r			3rd
s	t	a	g	n	a	n	t		4th
s	t	a	i	n	l	e	s	s	5th

11 **harpoon**

h	a	r	e	l	i	p		1st
h	a	r	m	o	n	i	c	2nd
h	a	r	n	e	s	s		3rd
h	a	r	p	o	o	n		4th
h	a	r	r	i	e	r		5th

12 **largesse**

l	a	p	w	i	n	g		1st
l	a	r	c	e	n	y		2nd
l	a	r	d	e	r			3rd
l	a	r	g	e	s	s	e	4th
l	a	r	v	a				5th

13 **EEL** wheel
14 **AIR** hair
15 **AND** standing
16 **HER** cherries
17 **PI, SF** The first letter moves forward three places. The second letter moves backwards three places.
18 **GF, IH** Both letters move forward two places.
19 **LS, MT** The first letters move forward one

place. The second letters are in a repeating pattern in alphabetical order: QQRRSST.
20 **DR, EQ** The first letters are in a repeating pattern in alphabetical order: BBCCDDE. The second letters are in reverse alphabetical order.

TEST 22: Mixed (page 23)

1 **win, lose** Only 'win, lose' are antonyms. The others are synonyms.
2 **warm, cool** 'Warm, cool' are direct opposites as both are neither hot or cold.
3 **clear, cloudy** If a day is 'clear' the sky shows blue. If it is 'cloudy' the sky is obscured.
4 **collect, deliver** 'Collect' is to take something from someone, whereas 'deliver' is to give something to them.
5 **11** $(7 \times 1) + 3 = 10$ and $(3 \times 5) + 3 = 18$, so $(4 \times 2) + 3 = 11$
6 **10** $(14 - 4) + 1 = 11$ and $(13 - 7) + 1 = 7$, so $(12 - 3) + 1 = 10$
7 **5** $(5 - 2) \times 5 = 15$ and $(7 - 6) \times 5 = 5$, so $(4 - 3) \times 5 = 5$
8 **6** $(6 + 7) - 5 = 8$ and $(7 + 4) - 5 = 6$, so $(8 + 3) - 5 = 6$
9 **dart** To 'dart' means to move quickly.
10 **fair** 'Fair' means light in colour; it also means honest or true.
11 **eject** To 'eject' is to throw out, get rid of.
12 **stout** 'Stout' is rounded and fat and well covered rather than light and flimsy.
13 **r** cane, bred
14 **p** light, carp
15 **t** sue, turn
16 **l** food, hilt
17 **SHAPES, PHASES**
18 **GRUNTS, STRUNG**
19 **STAPLE, PALEST**
20 **STALE, LEAST**

TEST 23: Mixed (page 24)

1–5 Category A contains stationery (**rubber, pen**). Category B contains trees (**beech, pine**). Category C contains items relating to the coast (**beach, seaweed**). Category D contains furniture (**bed, chair**). Category E contains fish (**perch, pike**).
6 **FAME**   7 **HEAT**   8 **PLAN**
9 **CATER**   10 **ADDER**
11 **thick** 'Thin' is skinny or narrow whereas 'thick' is wide or dense.
12 **difficult** 'Easy' is simple whereas 'difficult' is hard.
13 **empty** 'Full' is replete whereas 'empty' has nothing in it.

14 **uneven** 'Flat' is smooth and level whereas 'uneven' is bumpy or cratered.

15 **noisy** 'Quiet' is noiseless whereas 'noisy' is busy and loud.

16 **climb, ascend**   17 **concur, agree**

18 **healthy, well**   19 **arrow, dart**

20 **carpet, rug**

TEST 24: Mixed (page 25)

1 **library, bank** 'Books' are stored in a 'library' as 'money' is stored in a 'bank'.

2 **weekend, weekday** 'Saturday' is a day on the 'weekend' whereas 'Monday' is a working day during the week.

3 **bite, peck** 'Teeth' bite in the same way as birds' beaks 'peck'.

4 **pip, stone** Inside an 'apple' core there are pips in the same way as in the centre of a 'peach' there is a 'stone'.

5 **boat, bicycle** An 'oar' powers a rowing 'boat' in the same way a 'pedal' powers a 'bicycle'.

6 **GAME, SAME**   7 **PLAY, PRAY**

8 **SITE, MITE**   9 **BASH, BATH**

10 **FORK, FORT**   11 **spaceship**

12 **roadworks**   13 **honeycomb**

14 **bullseye**   15 **headlong**

16–20 Use a table to help you work out the information:

Total = 23	Type	Animal	Nationality
4	Soft	Goat	Welsh (2) English (2)
5	Soft	Cow	English (5)
2	Soft	Sheep	English (2)
12	Hard	Cow	Welsh (3) Irish (2) English (7)

16 **11**   17 **soft**   18 **7**

19 **5**   20 **16**

TEST 25: Mixed (page 26)

1 **headstrong, stubborn** Both the words mean inflexible or mulish.

2 **border, edge** Both the words mean rim or perimeter.

3 **edgy, tense** Both words mean nervous or apprehensive.

4 **mutiny, revolt** Both words mean a rebellion.

5 **power, strength** Both words mean control, force or dominance.

6–10 Try each of the words in the first set of brackets. Do they make sense with any words in the second (and sometimes third) set of brackets? Only one combination of words makes sense.

6 **music, radio**

7 **spoke, telephone**

8 **leave, books, teacher**

9 **hippo, rivers, mouth**

10 **brushes, morning, flannel**

11 **DM, HQ** Both letters move forwards one place.

12 **GT, LO** The first letter is moves forwards one place, in alphabetical order. The second letter moves backwards one place, in reverse alphabetical order.

13 **GS, HQ** The first letter is a repeat pattern: FFGGHH. The second letter moves backwards two places.

14 **515, 533** The numbers increase by 9.

15 **10, 23** This is an alternating pattern. The first, third and fifth numbers increase by 3. The second, fourth, sixth and eighth numbers increase by 10.

16 **26, 28** This is an alternating pattern. The first, third and fifth numbers increase by 2. The second, fourth, sixth and eighth numbers increase by 1.

17 **land** landowner, landfill, landlady, landmark

18 **wild** wildlife, wildcat, wildfowl, wildfire

19 **high** highness, highlighter, highlight, highland

20 **wind** windswept, windsurfing, windscreen, windpipe

TEST 26: Mixed (page 27)

1 **s** lass, soak

2 **b** grub, book

3 **n** run, newt

4 **p** cramp, pole

5 **e** kite, else

6–8

P	I	E	C	E
R	■	D	■	A
E	A	G	E	R
E	■	E	■	L
N	O	S	E	Y

9–11

F	L	A	S	H
I	■	N	■	O
R	I	G	H	T
E	■	L	■	E
S	T	E	A	L

12 **Where** did you **put** the car keys?

13 Sam promised to **get** up early in the **morning**.

14 The batsman hit the **ball** over the **pavilion**.

15 He found a **book** he really liked on a **table**.

16 **hero** My uncle says you must take t**he ro**ugh with the smooth.

17 **hall** The teacher was very angry wit**h all** the class.
18 **rest** Mrs Blewitt says they **are st**ored in her greenhouse.
19 **tall** Mandy has gone to collec**t all** the hockey balls.
20 **here** A young swallow has migrated with t**he re**st of the birds.

TEST 27: Mixed (page 28)

1–3 Make an alphabetical list of the months.

April	June
August	March
December	May
February	November
January	October
July	September

1 **October**   2 **December**   3 **March**

4–7 Use a grid to help you.

B	O	T	T	L	E
A	N	S	S	K	D

Note the relationship between the code and the word 'BOTTLE'. To get from the word to the code, move each letter backwards one place.

4 **ODMBHK** P = O, E = D, N = M, C = B, I = H, L = K
5 **BQZXNM** C = B, R = Q, A = Z, Y = X, O = N, N = M
6 **SPOONS** R = S, O = P, N = O, N = O, M = N, R = S
7 **PLATES** O = P, K = L, Z = A, S = T, D = E, R = S
8 **26 31** The numbers increase by 5.
9 **11, 8** This is an alternating pattern. The first, third, fifth and seventh numbers increase by 1. The second, fourth and sixth numbers also increase by 1.
10 **16, 64** The number doubles each time.
11 **20, 5** This is an alternating pattern. The first, third, fifth and seventh numbers increase by 2. The second, fourth, sixth and eighth numbers decrease by 2.
12 **touch, feel** Both words are describing the senses.
13 **nail, tack** Both words refer to a type of metal fixing, hit by a hammer.
14 **oar, paddle** Both words are a means of powering or manoeuvring a boat.
15 **teacher, instructor** Both words refer to a person who is able to impart knowledge to a student.
16 **blackberry**   17 **armchair**   18 **roundabout**
19 **pillowcase**   20 **hedgerow**

TEST 28: Mixed (page 29)

1 **fair** 'Fair' means impartial as well as yellow- or pale-haired.
2 **right** 'Right' means accurate as well as to repair or make good.
3 **plain** 'Plain' means basic or natural as well as to make obvious and understandable.
4 **rich** 'Rich' means to have a lot of money as well as strong in flavour quite often in an overpowering way.
5 **9** 3 + 2 + 4 = 9
6 **10** (10 ÷ 2) + 5 = 10
7 **6** (3 × 10) ÷ 5 = 6
8 **8** (10 − 3) + (5 − 4) = 8
9 **shot** If you pu**sh ot**her people out of the way, you will be punished.
10 **mean** Ruby's new bike had a black fra**me an**d a white saddle.
11 **test** It takes forty minu**tes t**o cook my lasagne.
12 **tilt** She counted the hours un**til t**he bell rang.
13 **OUR** journey
14 **EAR** beard
15 **TEA** steam
16 **TEN** beaten
17 **swallow** There is only one 'W' in 'PILLOWCASE'.
18 **teacher** There is only one 'E' in 'CHARACTER'.
19 **cross** There is only one 'S' in 'CHROMOSOME'.
20 **noise** There is no 'E' in 'TRANSITION'.

TEST 29: Mixed (page 30)

1 **al** petal, alter
2 **le** handle, hedge
3 **fe** knife, fearless
4 **th** mouth, thorn
5 **PINES**   6 **PLEAT**
7 **CLASP**   8 **TRUST**
9–12 Category A: **Brian, Susan**
Category B: **bus, train**
Category C: **squash, beer**
Category D: **for, under**
13 **azure** 'Azure' is a shade of 'blue'.
14 **tranquil** 'Tranquil' means 'calm' or peaceful.
15 **weep** 'Weep' is to 'cry' or shed tears.
16 **bristle** 'Bristle' is a short length of hair or stem like 'stubble'.
17 **8** When the brother was born, the speaker was 4 and their father 32 (4 × 8). Add 8 years to the father's age, the newborn brother will be 8.
18 **12** The brother is 4 years younger than the speaker. If the speaker is 16, the brother will be 12 (16 − 4).

19 **10** (Z × 2) − 2, then divide by 3 = 6. Work backwards, doing the opposite. 6 × 3 = 18. Then add 2 = 20. Divide 20 by 2 = 10.

20 **13** (Z × 2) − 8, then divide by 3 = 6. Work backwards, doing the opposite. 6 × 3 = 18. Then add 8 = 26. Divide 26 by 2 = 13.

TEST 30: Mixed (page 31)

1–3 Try each of the words in the first set of brackets. Do they make sense with any words in the second and third set of brackets? Only one combination of three words makes sense.
1 **tennis, racquet, court**
2 **goldfish, swam, pondweed**
3 **weather, rainy, ground**
4–8 Mum, Sarah and Tom are next door to each other so they must be 3, 4, 5. If Pete is opposite Tom, then Tom must be 5 and Pete 12. Dad and Sarah are even numbers so Dad 14 and Sarah 4, leaving Mum in 3.
4 **Mum**   5 **Sarah**
6 **Tom**   7 **Pete**
8 **Dad**   9 **grief**
10 **cute**   11 **shake** or **quake**
12 **pride**   13 **trend**   14 **gush**
15–20 Three of the codes start with 9, so 9 = S. 0643 therefore = WANT. 9884 must be SOON. From this you can match all the code numbers to letters.
15 **9064** S = 9, W = 0, A = 6, N = 4
16 **9884** S = 9, O = 8, O = 8, N = 4
17 **0643** W = 0, A = 6, N = 4, T = 3
18 **9480** S = 9, N = 4, O = 8, W = 0
19 **TOWN** 3 = T, 8 = O, 0 = W, 4 = N
20 **ANTS** 6 = A, 4 = N, 3 = T, 9 = S

TEST 31: Mixed (page 32)

1–5 Use grids as shown below to help work out the missing word.

1 **PEAR**

3*		1	2	3*	4	
S	I	Z	E	S	T	U	N

3*		1	2	3*	4	
T	Y	P	E	A	R	C	H

2 **STOP**

		2	1			3/4*	3/4*
T	R	I	P	T	E	L	L

		2	1			3/4*	3/4*
F	A	T	S	D	R	O	P

3 **KING**

	2/3*	2/3*	1	2/3*		4	
S	E	E	R	E	N	D	S

	2/3*	2/3*	1	2/3*		4	
W	I	C	K	N	A	G	S

4 **TEAL**

2/3*			1	4	2/3*		
E	B	B	S	N	E	W	T

2/3*			1	4	2/3*		
E	M	I	T	L	A	M	B

5 **SPUR**

	3	2	1	4			
F	E	U	D	T	R	A	M

	3	2	1	4			
C	U	P	S	R	O	U	T

6 **complete, start** To 'start' is to begin whereas 'complete' is to finish.
7 **expose, conceal** 'Expose' is to show whereas 'conceal' is to hide.
8 **distant, approachable** 'Distant' is far away or aloof whereas 'approachable' is closer by and more open-minded.
9 **genuine, fake** 'Genuine' is real whereas 'fake' is a copy or imitation.
10 **praise, criticise** 'Praise' is to commend or approve whereas 'criticise' is to find fault with.
11 **D** A, B and C may or may not be true. They must be rejected because you must only use the information you are given.
12 **8** (10 × 4) ÷ 5 = 8
13 **2** (4 + 3) − (10 − 5) = 2
14 **5** (4 × 5) ÷ 10 + 3 = 5
15 **31** (4 − 3) + (10 × 3) = 31
16 **ACILPST**   17 **ACEMPRS**
18 **ADEIMNRSU**   19 **ABDEKORY**   20 **E**

TEST 32: Mixed (page 33)

1 **f** staff, foxes; cliff, fades
2 **g** stag, glue; frog, greet
3 **n** train, night; toxin, nails
4 **w** jaw, wail; straw, when
5 **evening, morning** 'Dusk' occurs in the 'evening' in the same way 'dawn' occurs in the morning.
6 **navy, ruby** 'Navy' is a shade of 'blue' in the same way 'ruby' is a shade of 'red'.
7 **truth, belief** A 'fact' is a 'truth' in the same way an 'opinion' is a 'belief'.
8 **drop, lower** 'Fall' is a synonym of 'drop' in the same way as 'descend' is a synonym of 'lower'.

9 **WALL, WILL**   10 **TRAP, TRIP**
11 **LIFE, LIME**   12 **SHOT, SOOT**
13 **homework**   14 **eggshell**
15 **backwards**   16 **grandstand**
17 **ankle** These words are all joints in the body.
18 **look** These are all synonyms describing ways of using your eyes and sight.
19 **London** These are all capital cities of Great Britain.
20 **instruct** These are all synonyms meaning to teach.

TEST 33: Mixed (page 34)

1 **EASEL, LEASE**   2 **THROW, WORTH**
3 **SPORE, PROSE**
4 **U\W** Both letters move forward four places. The / becomes \ in the second grouping.
5 **P70** The letters move forward one place. The numbers increase by 5.
6 **v37X** Both sets of letters (lower case and upper case) move forward four places. The numbers increase by 6.
7 **YxW** All the letters move backwards three places.
8 **SR** Both letters move backwards four places.
9 **T – W** Both letters move forwards six places. The + in the first pair becomes – in the second pair.
10 **bed** bedtime, bedclothes, bedroom, bedspread
11 **black** blackboard, blacklist, blackmail, blackbird
12 **life** lifetime, lifelong, lifeblood, lifeless
13 **some** something, someone, somewhere, somewhat
14–16 Try each of the words in the first set of brackets. Do they make sense with any words in the second and third set of brackets? Only one combination of three words makes sense.
14 **hard, banks, road**
15 **bed, pyjamas, hair**
16 **cinema, hurry, film**
17 **i** $(12 \times 5) \div 10 + 4 = 10$ $10 = i$
18 **m** $(10 + 3 + 2) - 12 = 3$ $3 = m$
19 **j** $(4 \times 4) - (2 \times 2) = 12$ $12 = j$
20 **n** $(12 \div 3) - (10 \div 5) = 2$ $2 = n$

TEST 34: Mixed (page 35)

1 **OPQ, WXY** Each letter moves forward four places.
2 **37, 33** This is an alternating pattern. The first, third, fifth and seventh numbers decrease by 11. The second, fourth, sixth and eighth numbers increase by 10.
3 **G24, O48** The letters move forwards two places and alternate between lower case and capital letters. The numbers increase by 6.
4 **10, 15** The number added increases by 1 each time: +3, +4, +5, +6, +7, +8, + 9. So, 6 + 4 = 10, 10 + 5 = 15.
5 **strong** 'Strong' means well developed and strapping and also level and firm.
6 **interior** 'Interior' is the inside of something as well as the very middle, or heart of something.
7 **coach** A 'coach' is a teacher and to 'coach' means to instruct.
8 **interest** An 'interest' could be something that occupies your free time; it can also be the mental quality you direct towards something you want to know about.
9 **listen**   10 **plain**
11 **tracing**   12 **stammer**
13 **AND** handle
14 **OAT** goats
15 **HAM** shampoo
16 **NET** magnetic
17 **c** cash, cart, chart, chair, clap
18 **p** parched, pill, pinched, prim, pale
19 **n** narrow, nearly, neither, neat, nail
20 **o** open, opal, owing, orange, oat

TEST 35: Mixed (page 36)

1 **ASLEEP**   2 **PRIEST**
3 **TRELLIS**   4 **SPADES**
5 **STREAM**   6 **SHEARS**
7 **SHALLOW**   8 **BELLOW**
9 **crow, clock** The other words all mean a panic or fear.
10 **rubber, ruler** The other words are writing implements.
11 **classroom, teacher** The other words are school subjects.
12 **cube, pyramid** The other words are two-dimensional shapes.
13 **four, three** A 'chair' has 'four' legs whereas a 'stool' has 'three' legs.
14 **scales, fur** 'Fish' have 'scales' in the same way a 'bear' has 'fur'.
15 **lid, roof** A 'lid' is the top or covering of a 'box' in the same way a 'roof' is the top or covering of the house.
16 **drive, beach** A 'drive' may be covered in 'gravel' in the same way a 'beach' may be covered in 'sand'.
17–20 Identify the first six letters of the alphabet: ABCDEF.
17 **efface**   18 **added**
19 **faced**   20 **dead**

TEST 36: Mixed (page 37)

1–4 Use a grid to help you.

C	H	R	I	S	T	M	A	S
*	!	/	%	?	\	£	:	?

1 **? ! % / ** S = ?, H = !, I = %, R = /, T = \
2 **£ : / * !** M = £, A = :, R = /, C = *, H = !
3 **STRICT** ? = S, \ = T, / = R, % = I, * = C, \ = T
4 **ASSIST** : = A, ? = S, ? = S, % = I, ? = S, \ = T

5–6 Use a grid to help you. Look carefully at the relationship between the letters and their number codes. Note that A = 1, B = 2, D = 4. Therefore, the numbers must correlate with the alphabetical places, eg C = 3, Z = 26 etc.

D	A	B	B	L	E
4	1	2	2	12	5

5 **3 1 2 12 5** C = 3, A = 1, B = 2, L = 12, E = 5
6 **6 1 3 5 4** F = 6, A = 1, C = 3, E = 5, D = 4

7–9

C	L	A	I	M	S
R		L			T
A	R	M	O	U	R
D		O			O
L		N			N
E	N	D	I	N	G

10–12

B	U	S	T	L	E
O		U		A	
U	D	D	E	R	S
N		D		G	
D	E	E	P	E	R
S		N		R	

13 **your** Dad asked me if I knew wh**y our** radio was broken.
14 **rent** My aunt took her child**ren t**o the theme park.
15 **stem** Deborah'**s tem**per got the better of her in class.
16 **done** The police raide**d one** address in Birmingham.

17–20 Draw a diagram to help you.

Bourne	North	Ashley
West		East
Dalton	South	Calne

17 **Bourne**
18 **Dalton**
19 **south**
20 **south-east**

TEST 37: Mixed (page 38)

1 **PLAY, SLAY**
2 **TYRE, TORE**
3 **CLOP, CROP**
4 **FOUL, FOOL**
5 **b** brain, blend, brake, beast, band
6 **l** lend, lout, lever, learn, lawful
7 **a** ascent, amaze, awake, ashore, ajar
8 **g** glad, gorge, gamble, glisten, grange
9 **MN** The first letter moves forwards five places. The second letter moves backwards five places.
10 **UWZ** Each of the letters moves forwards seven places.
11 **caterpillar, leaf** A 'butterfly' drinks 'nectar' as a 'caterpillar' eats a 'leaf'.
12 **fast, hare** A 'tortoise' moves slowly as a 'hare' moves 'fast'.
13 **I28** The letters move backwards three places. The numbers increase by 3.
14 **; / $ @** The symbols are reversed in the second grouping.
15 **gun, bullet** An 'arrow' is fired from a 'bow' as a 'bullet' is fired from a 'gun'.
16 **time, clock** 'Speed' is measured on a 'speedometer' as 'time' is measured on a 'clock'.
17 <u>**Sally**</u> feeds her <u>**guinea-pigs**</u> every day before breakfast.
18 For lunch today, we had roast <u>**chicken**</u> followed by fruit <u>**salad**</u>.
19 I am <u>**finding**</u> my <u>**maths**</u> homework hard.
20 My favourite <u>**television**</u> programme <u>**starts**</u> at 8.00pm.

TEST 38: Mixed (page 39)

1 **plate** The pattern is to remove the last letter from the first word and replace it with 'te'.
2 **plant** The pattern is to remove the third, fourth and fifth letters of the first word.
3 **rout** The pattern is to remove the 'a' from the first word and replaced it with 'ou' in the second word.
4 **bug** The pattern is to remove the middle 'd' and the final 'e' from the first word.
5 **blown** The pattern is two replace the first two letters of the first word, 'fr', with 'bl' in the second word.
6 **narrow** 'Short' and 'tall' are antonyms. The opposite of 'wide' is 'narrow'.
7 **over** 'Through' and 'around' are antonyms. The opposite of 'under' is 'over'.
8 **speak** 'Chatter', 'babble' are synonyms, as are 'talk' and 'speak'
9 **illuminate** 'Delicate' and 'flimsy' are synonyms. 'Light' and 'illuminate' are also synonyms.
10 **fasten** 'Laces' are 'tied' in the same way as 'buttons' are 'fastened'.

11 **40, 24** This is an alternating pattern. The first, third, fifth and seventh numbers decrease by 5. The second, fourth, sixth and eighth numbers increase by 4.

12 **11, 10** This is an alternating pattern. The first, third, fifth and seventh numbers increase by 3. The second, fourth, sixth and eighth numbers also increase by 3.

13 **t18, v31** The letters move forward one place. The number added increases by 1 each time: +2, +3, +4, +5, +6, +7, +8.

14 **GIT, HJS** The first two letters move forward one place. The third letter moves backwards one place.

15 **EHf, CFd** All the letters move forwards four places.

16–20 Use grids as shown below to help work out the missing word.

16 MOAT

		2	1			3		4
S	P	O	T		R	A	I	D

		2	1			3		4
B	O	O	M		S	A	L	T

17 DRIP

	3	2	1		4		
C	A	T	S		B	I	L	E

	3	2	1		4		
B	I	R	D		P	I	N	K

18 RAID

4*		2	1*		1*		3	4*
T	R	I	P		P	A	N	T

4*		2	1*		1*		3	4*
F	E	A	R		G	R	I	D

19 TAIL

	4	2/3*	1		2/3*		
S	L	O	W		P	O	S	H

	4	2/3*	1		2/3*		
S	L	A	T		K	I	L	L

20 DEAL

4	2*	3	1*		1*			2*
T	E	A	M		M	I	L	E

4	2*	3	1*		1*			2*
L	E	A	F		D	I	C	E

TEST 39: Mixed (page 40)

1–5 Use a table to help you.

	Naomi	Fern	Husna	Debra
Spanish	✓	✓	✓	
French		✓	✓	✓
Art	✓		✓	✓
Chemistry	✓	✓		✓
Greek		✓		
Geography		✓		✓
Textiles	✓			✓
Music		✓	✓	

1 Fern   **2** Naomi   **3** Husna
4 Debra   **5** Naomi

6–9 Use a grid to help you. Look carefully at the relationship between the letters and codes. To get from the word 'CANDLE' to the code, move each letter forwards two places.

C	A	N	D	L	E
E	C	P	F	N	G

6 **NKIJV** L = N, I = K, G = I, H = J, T = V

7 **FCTMPGUU** D = F, A = C, R = T, K = M, N = P, E = G, S = U, S = U

8 **LUCKY** N = L, W = U, E = C, M = K, A = Y

9 **CRAZY** E = C, R = T, A = C, Z = B, Y = A

10 **rigid, sturdy** These words are all synonyms and all mean much the same.

11 **defeat, conquer** These words are all synonyms and all mean much the same.

12 **inaccurate, false** These words are antonyms. The opposite of 'true' is 'false'.

13 **firm, harsh** 'Hard' and 'firm' are synonyms in the same way as are 'coarse' and 'harsh'.

14 **proud, arrogant** These words are antonyms. 'Modest' and 'humble' are the opposites of 'proud' and 'arrogant'.

15 **ADGHRTU**   **16** **CEMOPRTU**

17 **DRAWL, DRAWN, DREAM**

18 **HEARTH, HEARTY, HEATER**

19 **Saturday** Friday, Monday, <u>Saturday</u>, Sunday, Thursday, Tuesday, Wednesday

20 **R**

TEST 40: Mixed (page 41)

1 **12, 12** This is an alternating pattern. The first, third, fifth and seventh numbers increase by 6. The second, fourth, sixth and eighth numbers decrease by 3.

2 **ZAB, YBC** The first letter moves backwards one place. The second and third letters move forward one place.

3 **15b, 11a** The number subtracted decreases by 1 each time: –10, –9, –8, –7, –6, –5, –4. The letters move backwards one place.

4 **RSq, ZAy** All the letters move forwards four places.

5 **WORD, WARD**   6 **ROSE, RISE**
7 **LAZE, LAME**   8 **RICE, RISE**
9 **PURE, SURE**   10 **BEAT, BOAT**
11 **FLEA, FLEW**   12 **HOME, HOSE**

13 **w** wheel, what, wall, whale, weighty
14 **h** height, herring, heel, hedge, hearth
15 **p** potter, park, plight, phoney, prattle
16 **e** elope, eat, ebony, estate, event

17–20 From the information you know that Gretel is at the side of the theatre, therefore 2J. If Sandra sat directly three rows behind Pravin, then she must be in 4D and Pravin in 1D. Clement sits next to Pravin, therefore Clement = 1C. If Penelope sits diagonally in front of Sandra (4D) the Penelope = 3E. Judy sits next to her sister. Therefore, her sister must be Sandra (4D) so Judy = 4E. If Harold is closer to Kang rather than anyone else, he must be in 2G which would leave space around him, leaving Kang in 2F.

1C = Clement
1D = Pravin
2F = Kang
2G = Harold
2J = Gretel
3E = Penelope
4D = Sandra
4E = Judy

Puzzle 1 (page 42)

1–4 The key here is to look at the end of the words. Find a word that ends with a letter that is also at the beginning of a word. Once you have established those two words, you can place all of them.

1

P	R	I	Z	E
R		N		N
I	N	L	E	T
Z		L		E
E	N	T	E	R

2

A	W	A	R	E
W		C		N
A	C	R	I	D
R		I		E
E	N	D	E	D

3

S	A	L	T	S
A		I		T
L	I	V	E	R
T		E		A
S	T	R	A	P

4

B	A	T	O	N
A		A		E
T	A	U	P	E
O		P		D
N	E	E	D	S

5–10 Look at the first letters of all the words. Rearrange them to make one of the words. You will now have found the first word across and down.

5

M	E	A	T
E	A	C	H
A	C	H	E
T	H	E	N

6

D	A	I	S
A	U	N	T
I	N	T	O
S	T	O	P

7

P	R	A	Y
R	A	R	E
A	R	E	A
Y	E	A	R

8

S	I	G	N
I	D	E	A
G	E	R	M
N	A	M	E

9

E	A	G	E	R
A	L	O	N	E
G	O	U	D	A
E	N	D	E	D
R	E	A	D	S

10

S	T	A	M	P
T	H	R	E	E
A	R	E	A	S
M	E	A	N	T
P	E	S	T	O

Puzzle 2 (page 43)

Look at the clues and solve as many as you can. Position them on the lily pads so that one letter is altered each time. If you cannot work out the word looking at the clue, go to the lily pads and replace one letter at a time to make a new word and see if you can identify the clues.

1 PARK, PACK, SACK   3 MOAN, MOON, MOOR   5 CROW, BROW, BLOW
2 BELT, BEST, BUST   4 PINT, MINT, MIST

Bond Verbal Reasoning 10 Minute Tests 10–11+ years

Puzzle 3 (page 44)

Fill in the grid with crosses as well as ticks as you go through the information.

You know that Grandpa was with a girl, so put a cross for James against Grandpa and one for Jamila and donkey rides. A tick for Clare for the ice creams and crosses for all the other options, as well as crosses for the other children and ice creams. You can also put a cross for Clare and Grandpa and Grandpa and ice creams. Learn that James was with his big sister, so tick for him and crosses for the others. Finally, you know Mum had fun playing beach games, so that can't be Clare or James as well. Put in the ticks and crosses and you will be able to deduce all the rest of the grid.

Ice creams must be Clare and her aunt. Put in the ticks and crosses and you can solve the grid.

	mum	grandpa	aunt	sister	funfair	donkey ride	ice cream	beach games
Lucy	x	✓	x	x	x	✓	x	x
Clare	x	x	✓	x	x	x	✓	x
James	x	x	x	✓	✓	x	x	x
Jamila	✓	x	x	x	x	x	x	✓
funfair	x	x	x	✓				
donkey ride	x	✓	x	x				
ice cream	x	x	✓	x				
beach games	✓	x	x	x				

	RELATIVE	TREAT
Lucy	grandpa	donkey ride
Clare	aunt	ice cream
James	sister	funfair
Jamila	mum	beach games

Puzzle 4 (page 45)

Look at the length of the words you have to fit into the grid. For example, if there is only one word of 8 letters long and only one space big enough, you can place that word. Once you have looked at that and exhausted the possibilities, look at your downwards space and see where the letters intersect the other horizontal words. Pick out the appropriate letters of those words. Are they likely to go next to each other in the downwards word? If not, try another one.

1 water
2 eating
3 sentence

Puzzle 5 (page 46)

Blend the consonants together and work round each of the letters in turn. When you have made one word, use it to rhyme other words (for example: late, sate, pate) or use the letters again in another order (for example: late, tale, teal). Try taking it in turns with the different letters and put different endings on them (for example: sea, set, sap, sat). To get longer words, think of the shape of the words, blending the consonants (pleat), splitting up the vowels (paste), putting the vowels together (least), making plurals with your 's' and so on.
Possible answers include:

6-letter: staple, pastel, petals, plates, pleats, palest

5-letter: stale, steal, tales, plate, pleas, slept, pleat, least, pelts, slate, splat, lapse, petal, pales

4-letter: last, salt, plea, slap, slat, pale, sale, late, tale, leap, seal, peal, pelt, lets, leas

3-letter: let, lap, pal, ale, lea

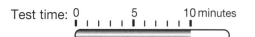

Complete the following sentences in the best way by choosing one word from each set of brackets.

Example Tall is to (tree, <u>short</u>, colour) as narrow is to (thin, white, <u>wide</u>).

1 Book is to (library, author, paper) as money is to (cash, bank, exchange).

2 Saturday is to (weekend, supermarket, holiday) as Monday is to (washing, weekday, school).

3 Tooth is to (bite, filling, mouth) as beak is to (nest, worms, peck).

4 Apple is to (wine, juice, pip) as peach is to (apricot, stone, tree).

5 Oar is to (mine, ship, boat) as pedal is to (bicycle, horse, pushers).

Change the first word into the last word by changing one letter at a time, and making two new, different words in the middle.

Example CASE ___CASH___ ___WASH___ WISH

6 GATE _____ _____ SOME   **7** PLAN _____ _____ PREY

8 SIZE _____ _____ MUTE   **9** BASK _____ _____ BOTH

10 WORK _____ _____ FONT

Underline two words, one from each group, that go together to form a new word. The word in the first group always comes first.

Example (hand, <u>green</u>, for)   (light, <u>house,</u> sure)

11 (old, space, fishing) (age, ship, boat)   **12** (road, lane, street)   (works, stop, gear)

13 (darling, honey, hare) (brush, hive, comb)   **14** (pigs, bulls, birds)   (eye, ear, nose)

15 (bread, stick, head) (short, long, wide)

From the information supplied, answer the questions.

There were 23 different types of cheese on a cheese counter at the farm shop.
There were four different types of soft goats' cheese, two of these were Welsh, the rest English.
There were seven other types of soft cheese; five cows' cheeses and two cheeses made from milk taken from sheep. All these were English.
There were 12 hard cows' cheeses, three from Wales and two from Ireland.

16 How many soft cheeses were there? _____

17 Are the sheep's cheeses soft or hard? _____

18 How many English hard cheeses were there? _____

19 How many Welsh cheeses were there altogether? _____

20 How many English cheeses were there altogether? _____

(25)

Total [   ]

Time for a break! Go to Puzzle Page 44 ▶

Underline the two words, one from each group, that are closest in meaning.

Example (race, shop, <u>start</u>)   (finish, <u>begin</u>, end)

1 (headlong, headstrong, headline)   (stubborn, lengthy, mark)
2 (clothes, line, border)   (flower, straight, edge)
3 (edgy, calm, sensible)   (tender, tense, hectic)
4 (pirate, mutiny, crew)   (revolt, repulse, revive)
5 (power, tower, mower)   (length, width, strength)

Complete the following sentences by selecting the most sensible word from each group of words given in the brackets. Underline the words selected.

Example The (<u>children</u>, boxes, foxes) carried the (houses, <u>books</u>, steps) home from the (greengrocer, <u>library</u>, factory).

6 My aunt listens to (music, tortoises, trees) on the (bathroom, radio, dustbin).
7 I (spoke, saw, ran) to Jo on the (television, park, telephone).
8 "Kindly (eat, leave, climb) those (tomatoes, stairs, books) alone!" shouted the (desk, teacher, goldfish).
9 A (hippo, giraffe, mouse) lives mostly in African (rivers, houses, airports) and has a big (ear, mouth, neck).
10 Before Adam (combs, counts, brushes) his teeth in the (classroom, morning, jungle) he likes to wash his face with his (flannel, hairbrush, dog).

A B C D E F G H I J K L M N O P Q R S T U V W X Y Z

Give the two missing groups of letters or numbers in the following sequences.
The alphabet has been written out to help you.

Example   CQ   DP   EQ   FP   <u>GQ</u>   <u>HP</u>

11	CL	___	EN	FO	GP	___	12	___	HS	IR	JQ	KP ___
13	FY	FW	GU	___	___	HO	14	506	___	524	___	542 551
15	17	___	20	20	___	30	26	40				
16	24	25	___	26	28	27	30	___				

Find a word that can be put in front of each of the following words to make a new, compound word.

Example cast   fall   ward   pour   <u>down</u>

17	owner	fill	lady	mark	_____
18	life	cat	fowl	fire	_____
19	ness	lighter	light	land	_____
20	swept	surfing	screen	pipe	_____

Total

Find the letter which will end the first word and start the second word.

Example peac (h) ome

1 las (__) oak

2 gru (__) ook

3 ru (__) ewt

4 cram (__) ole

5 kit (__) lse

Fill in the crosswords so that all the words are included.

6–8

EARLY NOSEY

EAGER PREEN

PIECE EDGES

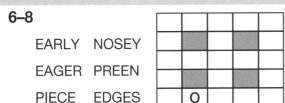

9–11

STEAL FLASH

HOTEL FIRES

ANGLE RIGHT

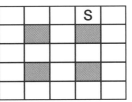

Find and underline the two words that need to change places for each sentence to make sense.

Example She went to <u>letter</u> the <u>write</u>.

12 Put did you where the car keys?

13 Sam promised to morning up early in the get.

14 The batsman hit the pavilion over the ball.

15 He found a table he really liked on a book.

Write the four-letter word hidden at the end of one word and the beginning of the next word. The order of the letters may not be changed.

Example We had bat<u>s and</u> balls.   *sand*

16 My uncle says you must take the rough with the smooth. _____

17 The teacher was very angry with all the class. _____

18 Mrs Blewitt says they are stored in her greenhouse. _____

19 Mandy has gone to collect all the hockey balls. _____

20 A young swallow has migrated with the rest of the birds. _____

Total _____

If the months were put in alphabetical order, which would be:

1 the second last month? _____

2 the third month? _____

3 the month after June? _____

A B C D E F G H I J K L M N O P Q R S T U V W X Y Z

The word BOTTLE is written in code as ANSSKD. Encode each of these words using the same code.

4 PENCIL _____   **5** CRAYON _____

Decode these words using the same code as above.

6 RONNMR _____   **7** OKZSDR _____

Give the two missing numbers in the following sequences.

Example CQ   DP   EQ   FP   _GQ_   _HP_

8	___	___	36	41	46	51		
9	5	9	6	10	7	___	___	
10	4	8	___	32	___	128		
11	16	9	18	7	___	___	22	3

Underline two words from the group which are most similar in type or meaning.

Example dear   pleasant   poor   extravagant   expensive

12	touch	feel	smoke	laugh	ring
13	hammer	nail	finger	tack	varnish
14	coal	gem	oar	majesty	paddle
15	neighbour	teacher	friend	niece	instructor

Underline two words, one from each group, that go together to form a new word. The word in the first group always comes first.

Example (hand, green, for)   (light, house, sure)

16 (sea, green, black)   (berry, current, piece)

17 (turn, right, arm)   (gate, stop, chair)

18 (ground, round, water)   (under, about, place)

19 (pillow, briefs, picnic)   (place, case, sheet)

20 (vegetable, grass, hedge)   (wood, green, row)

Total

Underline one word in brackets that will go equally well with both pairs of words outside the brackets.

Example rush, attack   cost, fee   (price, hasten, strike, <u>charge</u>, money)

1   just, equal   blonde, light   (fair, plus, yellow, appropriate, true)

2   correct, precise   fix, mend   (exact, wrong, right, sum, sort)

3   undecorated, simple   clear, direct   (easy, ugly, flat, plain, straight)

4   wealthy, affluent   unhealthy, creamy   (satisfactory, well, rich, correctly, strong)

If a = 2, b = 5, c = 4, d = 3 and e = 10, find the value of the following.

5 $d + a + c = $ _____   **6** $\dfrac{e}{a} + b = $ _____   **7** $\dfrac{de}{b} = $ _____   **8** $(e - d) + (b - c) = $ _____

Write the four-letter word hidden at the end of one word and the beginning of the next word. The order of the letters may not be changed.

Example We had bat<u>s and</u> balls.   _____ *sand* _____

9   If you push other people out of the way, you will be punished.   _____

10   Ruby's new bike had a black frame and a white saddle.   _____

11   It takes forty minutes to cook my lasagne.   _____

12   She counted the hours until the bell rang.   _____

Find the three-letter word that can be added to the letters in capitals to make a new word. The new word will complete the sentence sensibly. Write the three-letter word.

Example The cat sprang onto the MO.   _____ USE _____

13   The JNEY to Scotland took a long time.   _____

14   The old man had a long grey BD.   _____

15   Don't burn yourself on the SM from the kettle.   _____

16   The BEA finalist congratulated the winner.   _____

Underline the one word in each group that **cannot be made** from the letters of the word in capital letters.

Example STATIONERY   stone   tyres   ration   <u>nation</u>   noisy

17   PILLOWCASE   swallow   lapse   scalp   callow   scale

18   CHARACTER   crater   charter   earth   teacher   reach

19   CHROMOSOME   choose   morose   chrome   rooms   cross

20   TRANSITION   artist   nations   noise   strait   station

Total [   ]

TEST 29: **Mixed**

Test time: 0   5   10 minutes

Find two letters that will end the first word and start the second word.

Example pas ($\underline{t}$ $\underline{a}$) ste

1 pet (__ __) ter   2 hand (__ __) dge

3 kni (__ __) arless   4 mou (__ __) orn

Rearrange the letters in capitals to make another word. The new word has something to do with the first two words or phrases.

Example spot   soil   SAINT   <u>STAIN</u>

5	longs for	yearns	SNIPE	_____
6	fold	crease	PETAL	_____
7	clutch	pin part of a brooch	SCALP	_____
8	faith	belief	STRUT	_____

Look at these words. Sort them into groups.

9–12   Brian   bus   for   train   under   squash   Susan   beer

A Names	B Transport	C Drinks	D Prepositions
_____	_____	_____	_____
_____	_____	_____	_____

Underline the word in brackets closest in meaning to the word in capitals.

Example UNHAPPY   (unkind, death, laughter, <u>sad</u>, friendly)

13 BLUE (pink, bruise, sky, downfall, azure)   14 CALM (lake, rough, kind, tranquil, stormy)

15 CRY (whisper, weep, call, say, tearful)   16 STUBBLE (chin, field, straw, bristle, fall)

From the information supplied, complete the statements.

I was 4 when my brother was born. My father was 8 times older than I was then.

17 When my father is 40 my brother will be _____ years old.

18 When I am 16, my brother will be _____ years old.

From the information supplied, answer the questions.

Z is a number. Double it and take away 2. Divide by 3 and the answer is 6.

19 What is Z? _____

20 What would Z be if you take away 8 instead of 2? _____

---

(30)

Total [ ]

Complete the following sentences by selecting the most sensible word from each group of words given in the brackets. Underline the words selected.

Example The (<u>children</u>, boxes, foxes) carried the (houses, <u>books</u>, steps) home from the (greengrocer, <u>library</u>, factory).

1 The (tennis, football, golf) player lifted his (club, racquet, shirt) and hit the ball into the (yard, goal, court).

2 The (banana, goldfish, man) (swam, climbed, lay) around the bowl amongst the (pondweed, kitchen, salad).

3 The weather forecaster said the (rain, weather, cloud) would be (weather, rainy, map) this afternoon with snow on high (ground, tea, cloud).

From the information supplied, answer the questions.
A family went to the swimming baths and put their clothes in different lockers.
Mum, Sarah and Tom put their clothes in lockers next door to each other.
Pete put his in the locker opposite Tom's. Dad and Sarah used even numbered lockers.
The unavailable lockers are shaded. Who used which locker?

4 Locker 3 _____

5 Locker 4 _____

6 Locker 5 _____

7 Locker 12 _____

8 Locker 14 _____

1	2	3	4	5	6	7
8	9	10	11	12	13	14

Find a word that is similar in meaning to the word in capital letters and that rhymes with the second word.

Example CABLE tyre _wire_

9 MISERY beef _____

10 PRETTY suit _____

11 QUIVER brake _____

12 CONCEIT wide _____

13 FASHION friend _____

14 POUR thrush _____

Here are the number codes for four words.
9480 0643 9064 9884
Match the right code to the right word.

15 SWAN _____ 16 SOON _____ 17 WANT_____ 18 SNOW _____

Decode these words using the same code as above.

19 3804 _____ 20 6439 _____

Total

Look at the first group of three words. The word in the middle has been made from the two other words. Complete the second group of three words in the same way, making a new word in the middle of the group.

Example PAIN INTO TOOK   ALSO _SOON_ ONLY

1	SIZE	ZEST	STUN	TYPE	_____	ARCH
2	TRIP	PILL	TELL	FATS	_____	DROP
3	SEER	REED	ENDS	WICK	_____	NAGS
4	EBBS	SEEN	NEWT	EMIT	_____	LAMB
5	FEUD	DUET	TRAM	CUPS	_____	ROUT

Underline the two words, one from each group, which are the most opposite in meaning.

Example (dawn, <u>early</u>, wake)   (<u>late</u>, stop, sunrise)

6	(complete, compete, compel)	(entire, start, win)
7	(hide, expose, cruise)	(depose, conceal, decrease)
8	(stately, friendly, distant)	(approachable, anger, dislike)
9	(dead, genuine, alive)	(real, blunt, fake)
10	(praise, practise, prance)	(criticise, compliment, commend)

From the information supplied, underline the one statement below it that must be true.

11 Sheena was given a pot plant. It was not watered so it died.

    A The plant was a birthday present.   **C** Sheena liked plants.

    B Sheena was too busy to water the plant. **D** The plant needed water to stay alive.

If a = 10, b = 4, c = 3 and d = 5, find the value of the following.

12 $\dfrac{ab}{d}$ = ___   **13** $(b + c) - (a - d)$ = ___   **14** $\dfrac{bd}{a} + c$ = ___   **15** $(b - c) + ac$ = __

Write the letters in the following words in alphabetical order.

16 PLASTIC _____   **17** SCAMPER _____

18 NURSEMAID _____   **19** KEYBOARD _____

From the information supplied answer the question.

I appear twice in INNUMERABLE, once in SINCE and not at all in NATIONAL.

20 Which letter is being described? ____

Total

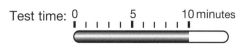

Find the one letter that will end the first word and start the second word of each pair of words. The same letter must be used for both pairs of words.

Example mea (t) able   fi (t) ab

1 staf (___) oxes   clif (___) ades   **2** sta (___) lue   fro (___) reet

3 trai (___) ight   toxi (___) ails   **4** ja (___) ail   stra (___) hen

Complete the following sentences in the best way by choosing one word from each set of brackets.

Example Tall is to (tree, <u>short</u>, colour) as narrow is to (thin, white, <u>wide</u>).

5 Dusk is to (sunset, evening, dark) as dawn is to (beginning, hours, morning).

6 Blue is to (sky, black, navy) as red is to (orange, blood, ruby).

7 Fact is to (truth, guess, idea) as opinion is to (proof, evidence, belief).

8 Fall is to (drop, water, autumn) as descend is to (lower, raise, winter).

Change the first word into the last word by changing one letter at a time, and making two new, different words in the middle.

Example CASE _CASH_   _WASH_   WISH

9 WALK _____ _____ PILL   **10** TRAY _____ _____ DRIP

11 LIFT _____ _____ LAME   **12** SHOE _____ _____ BOOT

Underline two words, one from each group, that go together to form a new word. The word in the first group always comes first.

Example (hand, <u>green</u>, for)   (light, <u>house</u>, sure)

13 (home, guest, hotel)   (going, work, bill)

14 (yolk, egg, soup)   (plate, pudding, shell)

15 (back, drake, lever)   (let, wards, for)

16 (low, high, grand)   (sit, stand, seat)

Underline the word in the brackets which goes best with the words given outside the brackets.

Example word, paragraph, sentence   (pen, cap, <u>letter</u>, top, stop)

17 elbow, shoulder, knee   (leg, arm, ankle, head, body)

18 peek, glance, peep   (mountain, sight, stare, eyes, look)

19 Belfast, Edinburgh, Cardiff   (Athens, Dublin, England, London, Iceland)

20 coach, train, drill   (engine, instruct, tool, man, rails)

(33)

Time for a break! Go to Puzzle Page 45 ▶

Total [   ]

Underline the two words that are made from the same letters.

Example TAP   PET   <u>TEA</u>   POT   <u>EAT</u>

1	EASEL	LEAST	SLATS	LEASE	STEEL
2	WORST	WRATH	THROW	WORTH	THREW
3	RASPS	SPORE	SPARE	PROSE	SPOON

A B C D E F G H I J K L M N O P Q R S T U V W X Y Z

Fill in the missing letters, symbols or numbers.

Example AB is to CD as PQ is to <u>RS</u> .

4   A/C is to E\G as Q/S is to _____.

5   G25 is to H30 as O65 is to _____.

6   f14H is to j20L as r31T is to _____.

7   HgF is to EdC as BaZ is to _____.

8   LK is to HG as WV is to _____.

9   M+P is to S – V as N+Q is to _____.

Find a word that can be put in front of each of the following words to make a new, compound word.

Example cast   fall   ward   pour   _down_

10	time	clothes	room	spread	_____
11	board	list	mail	bird	_____
12	time	long	blood	less	_____
13	thing	one	where	what	_____

Complete the following sentences by selecting the most sensible word from each group of words given in the brackets. Underline the words selected.

Example The (<u>children</u>, boxes, foxes) carried the (houses, <u>books</u>, steps) home from the (greengrocer, <u>library</u>, factory).

14   It was raining so (soft, slowly, hard) that the river burst its (banks, balloons, beds) and flooded the (crowd, road, river).

15   Before going to (school, church, bed) at night, Tracey puts on her (pyjamas, anorak, skis) and brushes her (shoes, carpets, hair).

16   We arrived late at the (cinema, ferry, shop) so had to (eat, rest, hurry) to see the beginning of the (book, film, concert).

If $i = 10$, $j = 12$, $k = 4$, $l = 5$, $m = 3$ and $n = 2$, find the value of the following. Write your answers as letters.

17   $\dfrac{jl}{i} + k =$ _____

18   $(i + m + n) - j =$ _____

19   $k^2 - n^2 =$ _____

20   $\dfrac{j}{m} - \dfrac{i}{l} =$ _____

Total

Test time: 0   5   10 minutes

A B C D E F G H I J K L M N O P Q R S T U V W X Y Z

Give the two missing groups of letters and numbers in the following sequences. The alphabet has been written out to help you.

Example CQ   DP   EQ   FP   *GQ*   *HP*

1	GHI	KLM	___	STU	___	ABC		
2	66	17	55	27	44	___	___	47
3	a6	C12	e18	___	i30	K36	m42	___
4	3	6	___	___	21	28	36	45

Underline one word in brackets that will go equally well with both pairs of words outside the brackets.

Example rush, attack   cost, fee   (price, hasten, strike, <u>charge</u>, money)

5	muscular, powerful	solid, stable	(frozen, strong, long-lasting, consistent, melted)
6	inner, inside	centre, core	(interior, inland, exterior, indoors, island)
7	instructor, tutor	teach, drill	(scout, bus, coach, student, learn)
8	hobby, activity	attention, curiosity	(interview, interfere, interest, intercept, intern)

Underline the one word in each group that **can be made** from the letters of the word in capital letters.

Example CHAMPION   camping   notch   peach   cramp   <u>chimp</u>

9	NESTLING	guest	slings	stink	gentle	listen
10	PINEAPPLE	ample	pliant	plain	planet	ripple
11	SCRATCHING	grate	tracing	strings	crouch	search
12	MAINSTREAM	straits	stammer	monster	strains	matter

Find the three-letter word that can be added to the letters in capitals to make a new word. The new word will complete the sentence sensibly. Write the three-letter word.

Example The cat sprang onto the MO.   _USE_

13	The door HLE has broken.	_____
14	We have lots of GS on our farm.	_____
15	The bottle of SPOO is in the bathroom.	_____
16	Some metals are MAGIC.	_____

Which one letter can be added to the front of all of these words to make new words?

Example _C_are   _C_at   _C_rate   _C_all   _C_lip

17 __ash __art __hart __hair __lap   **18** __arched __ill __inch __rim __ale

19 __arrow __early __either __eat __ail   **20** __pen __pal __wing __range __at

(35)

Total

TEST 35: **Mixed**

Test time: 0   5   10 minutes

Rearrange the letters in capitals to make another word. The new word has something to do with the first two words or phrases.

Example spot   soil   SAINT   STAIN _____

1	inattentive	not awake	PLEASE	_____
2	preacher	holy man	STRIPE	_____
3	framework	support for plants	TILLERS	_____
4	suit in cards	digging tools	PASSED	_____

Add one letter to the word in capital letters to make a new word. The meaning of the new word is given in the clue.

Example PLAN   simple   PLAIN _____

5	STEAM	a small river	_____
6	HEARS	a cutting tool	_____
7	SALLOW	not deep	_____
8	BELOW	to shout	_____

Underline the two words that are the odd ones out in each group of words.

Example black   <u>king</u>   purple   green   <u>house</u>

9	scare	crow	fright	shock	clock
10	pencil	rubber	ruler	pen	biro
11	history	geography	biology	classroom	teacher
12	cube	triangle	square	pyramid	rectangle

Complete the following sentences in the best way by choosing one word from each set of brackets.

Example Tall is to (tree, <u>short</u>, colour) as narrow is to (thin, white, <u>wide</u>).

13 Chair is to (four, six, two) as stool is to (kitchen, three, legs).

14 Fish is to (water, fin, scales) as bear is to (cub, fur, honey).

15 Box is to (cardboard, lid, label) as house is to (roof, chimney, upstairs).

16 Gravel is to (drive, stone, grey) as sand is to (castle, beach, Blackpool).

Underline any words below that contain only the first six letters of the alphabet.

17	coffee	beach	efface	dabble	dance
18	pebble	back	clubs	basin	added
19	fiction	freckle	fatigue	fudge	faced
20	abacus	dead	dread	cradle	adding

Total [ ]

Test time: 0 .... 5 .... 10 minutes

The code for the word CHRISTMAS is *!/%?\£:?. Encode each of these words using the same code.

1 SHIRT _____

2 MARCH _____

Decode these words using the same code as above.

3 ?\/%*\ _____

4 :??%?\ _____

The code for the word DABBLE is 4 1 2 2 12 5. Encode each of these words using the same code.

5 CABLE _____

6 FACED _____

Fill in the crosswords so that all the words are included.

7–9

			U		

10–12

			P		

CLAIMS   STRONG   ARMOUR

ENDING   ALMOND   CRADLE

DEEPER   LARGER   BOUNDS

SUDDEN   UDDERS   BUSTLE

Write the four-letter word hidden at the end of one word and the beginning of the next word. The order of the letters may not be changed.

Example We had bats <u>and</u> balls. _____*sand*_____

13 Dad asked me if I knew why our radio was broken. _____

14 My aunt took her children to the theme park. _____

15 Deborah's temper got the better of her in class. _____

16 The police raided one address in Birmingham. _____

From the following information, answer the questions.

The village of Ashley is due north of Calne and due east of the village of Bourne which, in turn, is due north of Dalton. The four villages make the corners of a square.

17 Which village is west of Ashley? _____

18 Which village is south of Bourne? _____

19 Which direction is Calne from Ashley? _____

20 Which direction is Calne from Bourne? _____

37

Total

TEST 37: **Mixed**

Test time: 0   5   10 minutes

Change the first word into the last word by changing one letter at a time, and making two new, different words in the middle.

Example CASE   <u>CASH</u>   <u>WASH</u>   WISH

1	PLAN	_____	_____	STAY
2	TYPE	_____	_____	SORE
3	CLIP	_____	_____	CROW
4	SOUL	_____	_____	FOOT

Which one letter can be added to the front of all of these words to make new words?

Example <u>C</u>are   <u>C</u>at   <u>C</u>rate   <u>C</u>all   <u>C</u>lip

5	__rain	__lend	__rake	__east	__and
6	__end	__out	__ever	__earn	__awful
7	__scent	__maze	__wake	__shore	__jar
8	__lad	__orge	__amble	__listen	__range

A B C D E F G H I J K L M N O P Q R S T U V W X Y Z

Fill in the missing symbols, letters or numbers, or underline the words.

Example AB is to CD as PQ is to <u>RS</u>.

9 AZ is to FU as HS is to ____.

10 ZBE is to GIL as NPS is to ____.

11 Butterfly is to nectar as (pillowcase, caterpillar, lion) is to (bed, leaf, pillow).

12 Slow is to tortoise as (flat, brush, fast) is to (hedgehog, pancake, hare).

13 T17 is to Q20 as L25 is to ____.

14 ?!£% is to %£!? as @$/; is to ____.

15 Bow is to arrow as (dart, gun, target) is to (bullet, gun, target).

16 Speed is to speedometer as (time, race, supersonic) is to (clock, car, jet).

Find and underline the two words that need to change places for each sentence to make sense.

Example She went to <u>letter</u> the <u>write</u>.

17 Guinea-pigs feeds her Sally every day before breakfast.

18 For lunch today we had roast salad followed by fruit chicken.

19 I am maths my finding homework hard.

20 My favourite starts programme television at 8.00pm.

38

Total

TEST 38: **Mixed**

Change the first word of the third pair in the same way as the other pairs to give a new word.

Example bind, hind   bare, hare   but, _hut_

1 quiz, quite   flux, flute   plan, _____
2 practice, price   stopping, sting   pleasant, _____
3 pat, pout   flat, flout   rat, _____
4 sludge, slug   fudge, fug   budge, _____
5 frame, blame   fright, blight   frown, _____

Look at the pair of words on the left. Underline the one word in the brackets that goes with the word outside the brackets in the same way as the first two words go together.

Example good, better   bad, (naughty, worst, <u>worse</u>, nasty)

6 short, tall   wide, (empty, fat, broad, narrow)
7 through, around   under, (beneath, over, next, by)
8 chatter, babble   talk, (quiet, silent, speak, noise)
9 delicate, flimsy   light, (illuminate, heavy, darken, substantial)
10 laces, tie   button, (chocolate, fasten, trousers, nose)

A B C D E F G H I J K L M N O P Q R S T U V W X Y Z

Give the two missing groups of letters and numbers in the following sequences.
The alphabet has been written out to help you.

11 45   16   ____   20   35   ____   30   28
12 4   8   7   ____   ____   14   13   17
13 p4   q6   r9   s13   ____   u24   ____   w39
14 ACZ   BDY   CEX   DFW   EGV   FHU   ____   ____
15 ADb   ____   ILj   MPn   QTr   UXv   YBz   ____   GJh

Look at the first group of three words. The word in the middle has been made from the two other words. Complete the second group of three words in the same way, making a new word in the middle of the group.

Example PA**IN**   INTO   **TO**OK   ALSO   _SOON_   ONLY

16 SPOT   TOAD   RAID   BOOM   _____   SALT
17 CATS   STAB   BILE   BIRD   _____   PINK
18 TRIP   PINT   PANT   FEAR   _____   GRID
19 SLOW   WOOL   POSH   SLAT   _____   KILL
20 TEAM   MEAT   MILE   LEAF   _____   DICE

Total

From the information supplied, answer the questions.

Naomi, Fern, Husna and Debra are friends at secondary school.

Fern, Naomi and Husna learn Spanish.   Husna, Fern and Debra study French.
Naomi, Husna and Debra study Art.   Debra, Fern and Naomi do Chemistry.
Husna learns Greek.   Fern and Debra do Geography.
Debra and Naomi do Textiles.   Fern and Husna do Music.

1   Who does French but does not do Art?   _____

2   Who does Chemistry but not Geography?   _____

3   Who does Art and Spanish but not Geography or Textiles? _____

4   Who does not study Music, Greek or Spanish?   _____

5   Who does the fewest subjects?   _____

A B C D E F G H I J K L M N O P Q R S T U V W X Y Z
The code for the word CANDLE is ECPFNG. Using the same code:

encode these words.

6   LIGHT   _____   **7**   DARKNESS   _____

decode these words.

8   NWEMA   _____   **9**   ETCBA   _____

Complete the following sentences in the best way by choosing one word from each set of brackets.

Example   Tall is to (tree, <u>short</u>, colour) as narrow is to (thin, white, <u>wide</u>).

10   Solid is to (jelly, fluid, rigid) as strong is to (liquid, weak, sturdy).

11   Thrash is to (scold, burn, defeat) as crush is to (conquer, draw, defy).

12   Accurate is to (inaccurate, straight, clever) as true is to (real, genuine, false).

13   Hard is to (possible, firm, slim) as coarse is to (dinner, harsh, smooth).

14   Modest is to (fashionable, proud, shut) as humble is to (meek, arrogant, lowly).

Write the following letters or words in alphabetical order.

15   DRAUGHT _____   **16**   COMPUTER _____

17   DREAM   DRAWN   DRAWL   _____

18   HEARTH   HEATER   HEARTY   _____

19   In alphabetical order, which day of the week comes after Monday? _____

From the information supplied, answer the question.

I appear twice in INCORRUPTIBLE, once in RIDDLE and not at all in PENCIL.

20   Which letter is being described? ____

40

Total

A B C D E F G H I J K L M N O P Q R S T U V W X Y Z

Give the two missing groups of letters and numbers in the following sequences. The alphabet has been written out to help you.

Example   CQ   DP   EQ   FP   *GQ*   *HP*

1 6   15   ___   ___   18   9   24   6

2 ___   ___   XCD   WDE   VEF   UFG   TGH   SHI

3 60h   50g   41f   33e   26d   20c   ___   ___

4 BCa   FGe   JKi   NOm   ___   VWu   ___   DEc

Change the first word into the last word by changing one letter at a time, and making two new, different words in the middle.

Example   CASE   *CASH*   *WASH*   WISH

5   WOOD _____ _____ WARE   **6** NOSE _____ _____ RICE

7   LAZY _____ _____ TAME   **8** MICE _____ _____ RISK

9   PYRE _____ _____ SURF   **10** BEST _____ _____ GOAT

11 PLEA _____ _____ FLOW   **12** COME _____ _____ HOST

Which one letter can be added to the front of all of the words to make new words?

Example *C*are   *C*at   *C*rate   *C*all   *C*lip

13 __heel   __hat   __all   __hale   __eighty

14 __eight __erring __eel   __edge   __earth

15 __otter __ark   __light __honey   __rattle

16 __lope   __at   __bony   __state   __vent

Eight people went to the theatre. The numbered seats are the ones they have tickets for. Using the information below, work out where each person sat.

Judy sat next to her sister.
Clement sat next to Pravin.
Gretel sat right at the side of the theatre.
Harold sat nearer Kang than anyone else.
Kang sat to the left of Harold.
Sandra sat directly three rows behind Pravin.
Penelope sat diagonally in front of Sandra.

FRONT

STAGE

LEFT   RIGHT

1C 1D
2F 2G   2J
3E
4D 4E
BACK

17–20   1C = _____   1D = _____

3E = _____   4D = _____   4E = _____

2F = _____   2G = _____   2J = _____

Time for a break! Go to Puzzle Page 46

Total

Puzzle

Take the words and place them in the grid so that each word reads horizontally and vertically.

Example

EVERY
BREAD
DOYEN

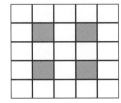

1

INLET
PRIZE
ENTER

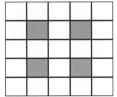

2

ENDED
ACRID
AWARE

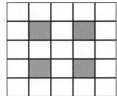

3

SALTS
STRAP
LIVER

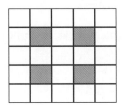

4

NEEDS
TAUPE
BATON

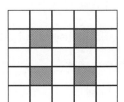

5

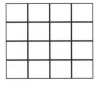

MEAT THEN
ACHE EACH

6

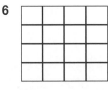

AUNT DAIS
STOP INTO

7

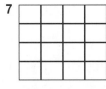

AREA RARE
PRAY YEAR

8

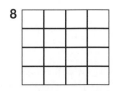

NAME SIGN
GERM IDEA

9

ALONE
EAGER
GOUDA
ENDED
READS

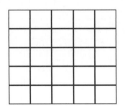

10

MEANT
PESTO
THREE
AREAS
STAMP

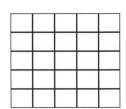

Puzzle ❷

Help Freddy to jump from one lily-pad to the next by changing one letter at a time. Watch out! The clues have been mixed up!

Example

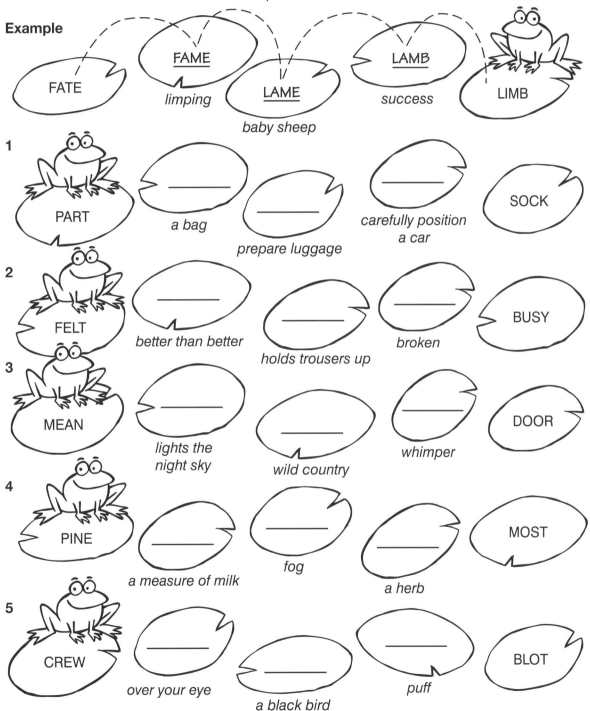

FATE

FAME

LAME
limping

baby sheep

LAMB
success

LIMB

1

PART

a bag

prepare luggage

carefully position a car

SOCK

2

FELT

better than better

holds trousers up

broken

BUSY

3

MEAN

lights the night sky

wild country

whimper

DOOR

4

PINE

a measure of milk

fog

a herb

MOST

5

CREW

over your eye

a black bird

puff

BLOT

Puzzle ③

Lucy, Clare, James and Jamila were all taken to Blackpool for a day trip over the summer holidays. Each of them was taken by an older relative. In the afternoon, before they went home, they were allowed one last treat.

From the information below, and using the grid to help you, work out which relative was with each child and what treat each of them chose. Fill in the table at the bottom of the page when you have worked it all out.

	mum	grandpa	aunt	sister	funfair	donkey ride	ice cream	beach games
Lucy								
Clare								
James		✗						
Jamila								
funfair				
donkey ride				
ice cream				
beach games				

Grandpa sat in a deck-chair while his granddaughter had a donkey ride.

Jamila was frightened of donkeys and did not want to go near them.

Clare was hungry and bought an ice cream with a female relative.

James and his big sister decided not to play beach games.

Mum had great fun playing beach games with her child.

	RELATIVE	TREAT
Lucy		
Clare		
James		
Jamila		

Puzzle 4

In the sets of words below, there is a word that links all the other words together.
This word reads vertically down the lightly shaded column of each grid.
The first one has been started for you. Place all the words into each grid
and then read down the lightly shaded column to find your linking word.

	S	N	O	W	F	L	A	K	E

FLOWER   BATHROOM   BARGE   SEASIDE   SNOWFLAKE

1 The linking word is: _____

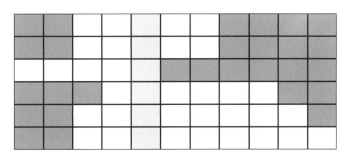

TEETH   DINNER   MUNCHING   ROAST   GRAVY   VEGETABLE

2 The linking word is: _____

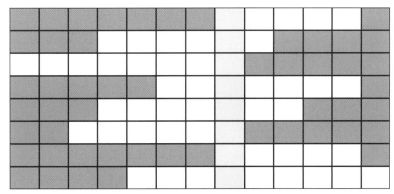

PRISON   COMMA   ARTICLE   ADJECTIVE   STORY
QUESTION   SUBJECT   LETTER

3 The linking word is: _____

Puzzle

Using the letters in the star, make as many words as you can. You must use the central letter every time and each letter only once. No two-letter words, initials or proper nouns are allowed. Good luck!

Example

priest	strip	ripe	sir
sprite		tire	rip
		rest	

For a good score aim to get: 2 x 6-letter words
8 x 5-letter words
8 x 4-letter words at least!

6-letter words

_____

_____

_____

_____

_____

_____

5-letter words

_____   _____

_____   _____

_____   _____

_____   _____

_____   _____

_____   _____

4-letter words

_____ _____

_____ _____

_____ _____

_____ _____

_____ _____

_____ _____

3-letter words

_____ _____ _____

_____ _____ _____

_____ _____ _____

_____ _____ _____

_____ _____ _____

_____ _____ _____

Progress Grid

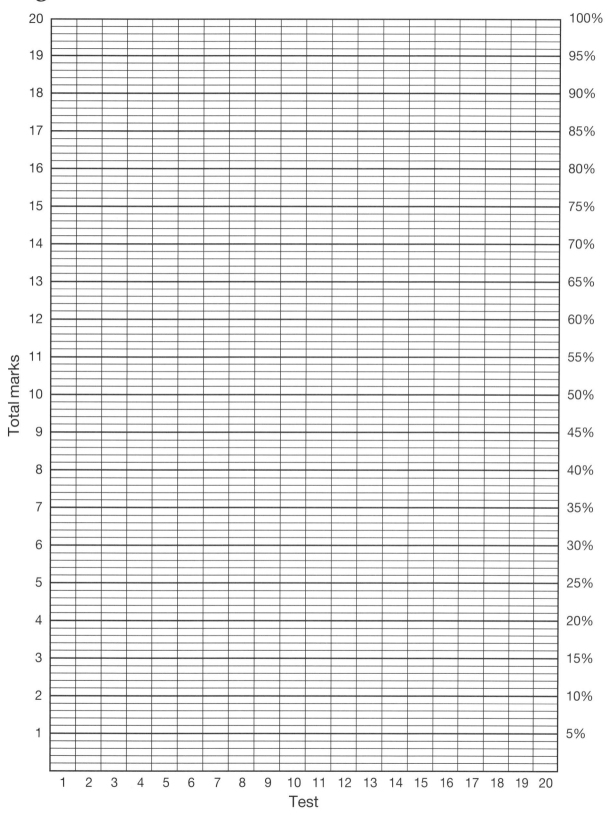

Progress Grid

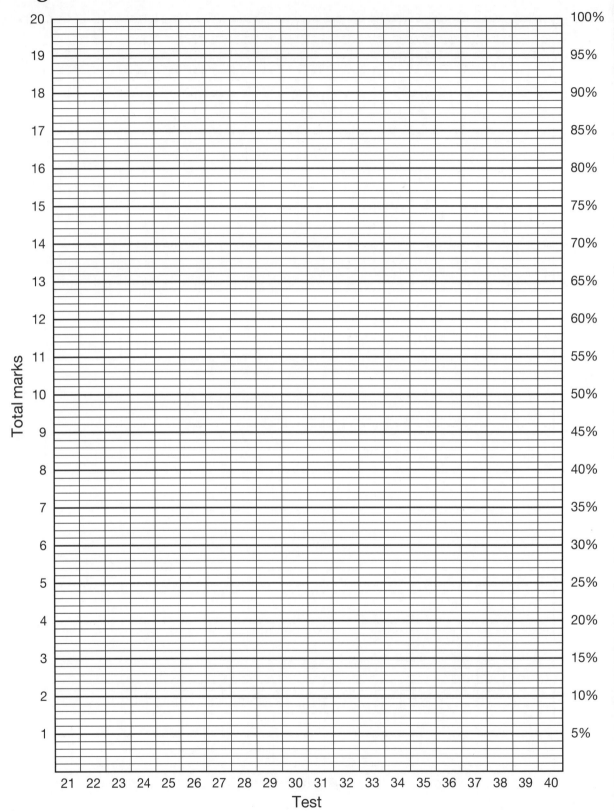

Total marks

Test

Non-verbal Reasoning

10 Minute Tests

10–11+ years

OXFORD

UNIVERSITY PRESS

Test time:

Which pattern continues or completes the given series?

Example

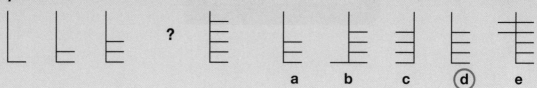

        a   b   c   (d)   e

1

a   b   c   d   e

2

a   b   c   d   e

3

a   b   c   d   e

4

a   b   c   d   e

5

a   b   c   d   e

6

a   b   c   d   e

Using the given patterns and codes, select the code that matches the last pattern.

Example

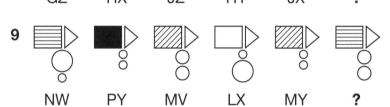

AX   AY   BZ   CY   BX   ?

AY   AX   CZ   BZ   BY
a   b   (c)   d   e

7

AD   AE   CE   BF   ?

AF   BE   CF   CD   BD
a   b   c   d   e

8

GZ   HX   JZ   HY   JX   ?

JY   JX   HZ   HY   GY
a   b   c   d   e

9

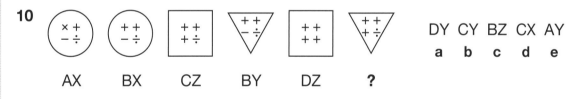

NW   PY   MV   LX   MY   ?

PX   LY   NV   MW   PV
a   b   c   d   e

10

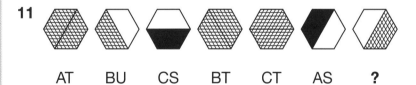

AX   BX   CZ   BY   DZ   ?

DY   CY   BZ   CX   AY
a   b   c   d   e

11

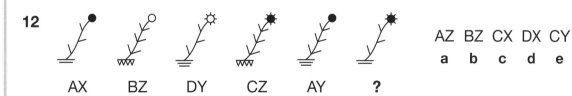

AT   BU   CS   BT   CT   AS   ?

BR   AT   CU   BS   AU
a   b   c   d   e

12

AX   BZ   DY   CZ   AY   ?

AZ   BZ   CX   DX   CY
a   b   c   d   e

Total

TEST 2: Codes and Analogies

Test time: 0 |||||5|||||10 minutes

Using the given patterns and codes, select the code that matches the last pattern.

Example

AX   AY   BZ   CY   BX   ?

AY AX CZ BZ BY
a   b   (c)   d   e

1

BX   CY   AZ   CX   DZ   ?

AX AY CZ DY BZ
a   b   c   d   e

2

ER   DR   ES   FR   FT   ?

ET FS DS DT ES
a   b   c   d   e

3

AH   BJ   AG   BK   CG   ?

CH BG CJ AK BH
a   b   c   d   e

4

LX   MY   LZ   NY   MZ   ?

LY NZ NX MX NY
a   b   c   d   e

5

AX   BY   CZ   BZ   DY   ?

CX CY BZ DZ AY
a   b   c   d   e

6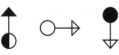

AY   BX   CZ   AX   BZ   DY   ?

AZ BY DX DZ CY
a   b   c   d   e

Which shape or pattern completes the second pair in the same way as the first pair?

Example

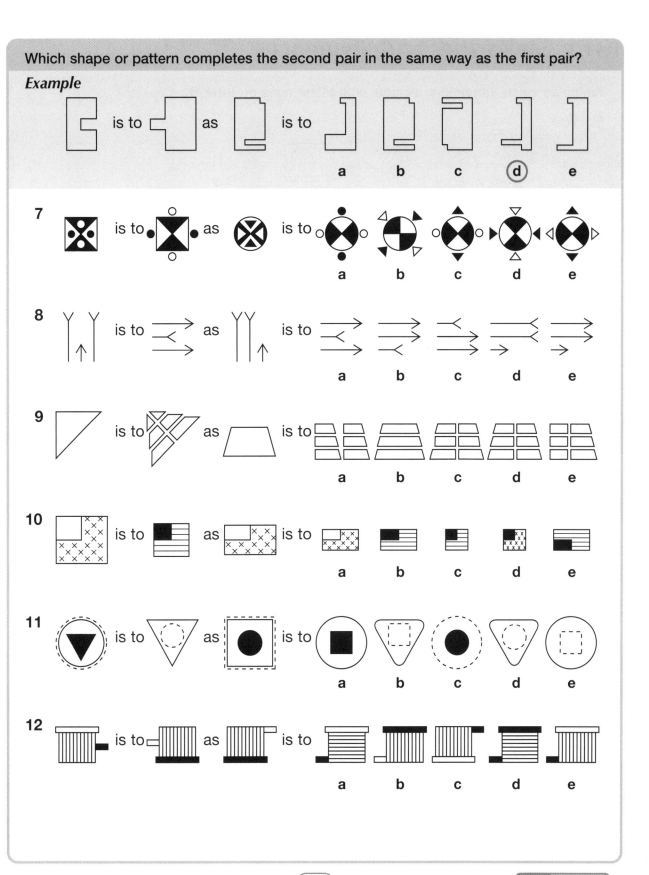

Total

TEST 3: **Similarities and Sequences**

Which shape on the right goes best with the shapes on the left?

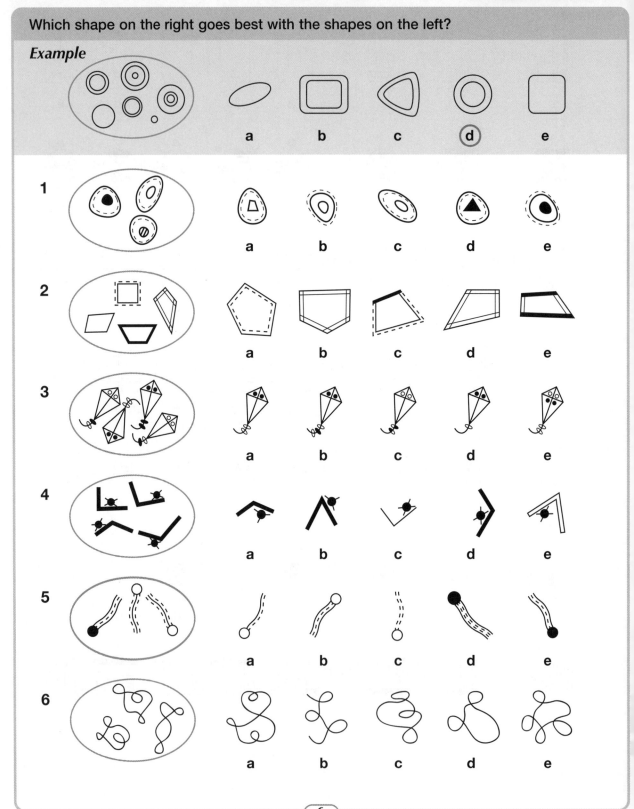

Example

                           a   b   c   d   e

1   a   b   c   d   e

2   a   b   c   d   e

3   a   b   c   d   e

4   a   b   c   d   e

5   a   b   c   d   e

6   a   b   c   d   e

Which shape or pattern completes the larger grid?

Example

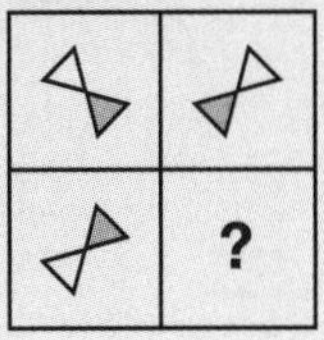

7

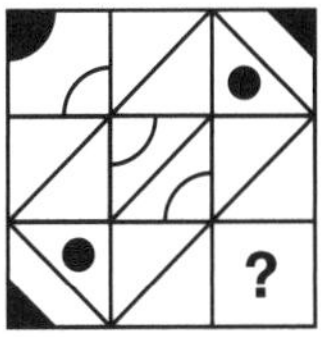

a   b   c   d   e

8

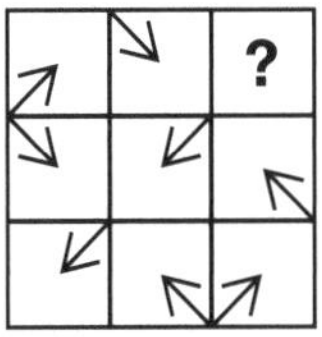

a   b   c   d   e

9

a   b   c   d   e

10

a   b   c   d   e

11

a   b   c   d   e

12

a   b   c   d   e

Total

TEST 4: Sequences and Codes

Which pattern continues or completes the given series?

Example

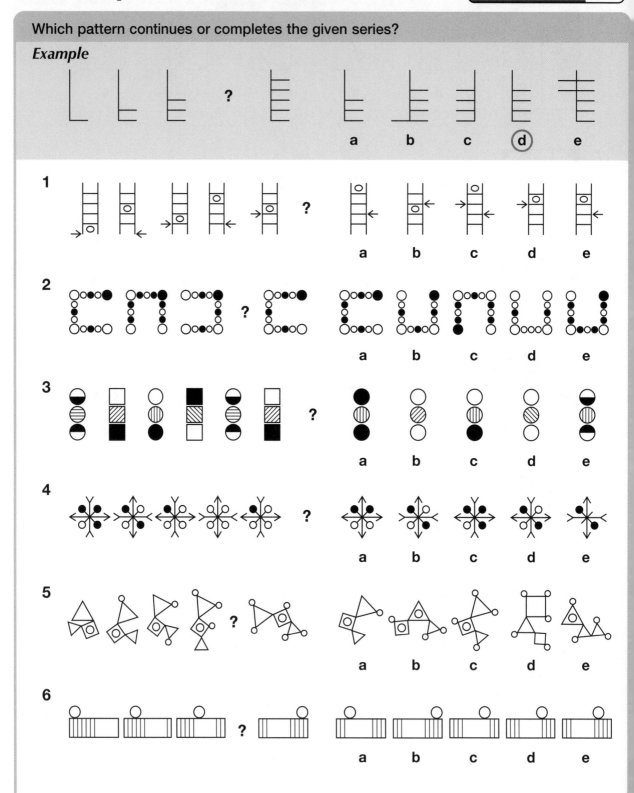

Using the given patterns and codes, select the code that matches the last pattern.

Example

					AY	AX	CZ	BZ	BY
					a	b	ⓒ	d	e

AX   AY   BZ   CY   BX   ?

7

ZR YS XS YQ ZQ
a   b   c   d   e

XP   YR   ZS   XQ   YP   ?

8

CN BN CL AO AL
a   b   c   d   e

AN   BM   BL   AM   CO   ?

9

DY CX CY AX DY
a   b   c   d   e

BX   CX   AY   DX   BY   ?

10

EL FN GN GM FM
a   b   c   d   e

FM   EM   GL   EN   FL   ?

11

AY BX CZ BY CY
a   b   c   d   e

AX   BY   AZ   CX   BZ   ?

12

CW EW VX EY DZ
a   b   c   d   e

DX   DW   EX   CZ   CY   ?

TEST 5: Cubes and Similarities

Test time: 0 |||||| 5 |||||| 10 minutes

Which cube could not be made from the given net?

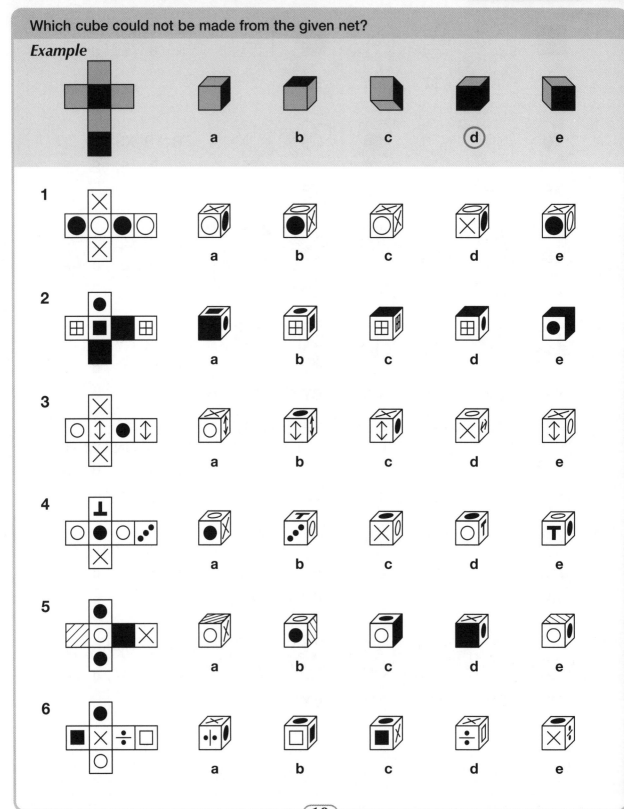

Example

a   b   c   (d)   e

1
a   b   c   d   e

2
a   b   c   d   e

3
a   b   c   d   e

4
a   b   c   d   e

5
a   b   c   d   e

6
a   b   c   d   e

10

Which shape on the right goes best with the shapes on the left?

Example

a   b   c   (d)   e

7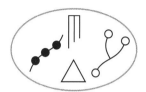

a   b   c   d   e

8

a   b   c   d   e

9

a   b   c   d   e

10

a   b   c   d   e

11

a   b   c   d   e

12

a   b   c   d   e

Total

TEST 6: Codes and Analogies

Using the given patterns and codes, select the code that matches the last pattern.

Example

AX   AY   BZ   CY   BX   ?

AY   AX   CZ   BZ   BY
a   b   (c)   d   e

1

AZ   BY   CZ   DX   AX   ?

CY   BX   CX   AY   DZ
a   b   c   d   e

2

BX   AX   CY   BZ   CX   ?

CZ   BY   AZ   AY   BX
a   b   c   d   e

3

DM   EN   FN   EL   FM   ?

DN   DL   EM   EL   FL
a   b   c   d   e

4

SE   SF   TG   TH   SG   ?

TE   SH   TH   SE   TF
a   b   c   d   e

5

PS   QW   PE   QN   QE   ?

QN   PW   PS   PN   QS
a   b   c   d   e

6

AG   CF   BE   AH   DG   ?

CH   BF   DF   DH   AF
a   b   c   d   e

Which shape or pattern completes the second pair in the same way as the first pair?

Example

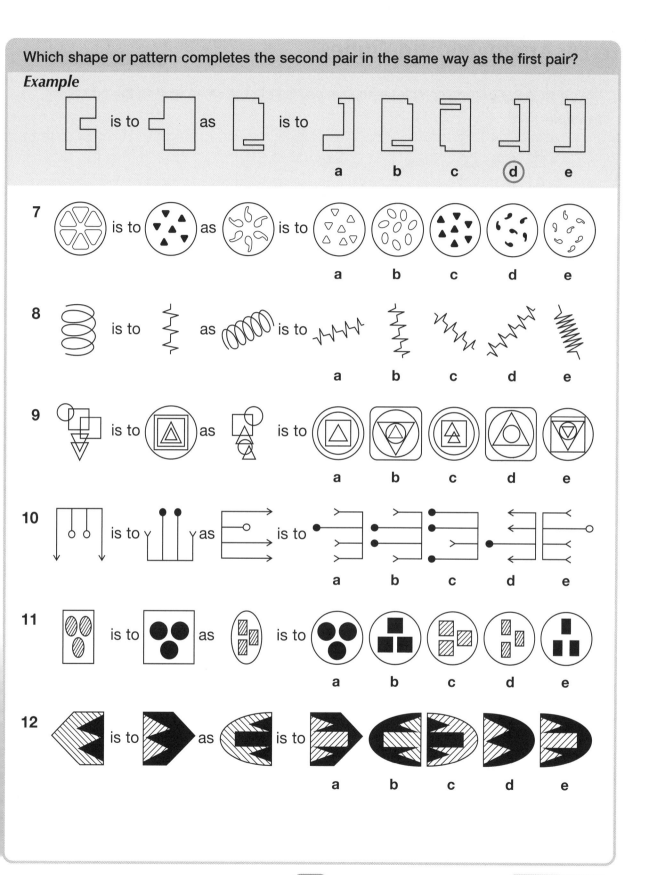

a   b   c   d   e

7

a   b   c   d   e

8

a   b   c   d   e

9

a   b   c   d   e

10

a   b   c   d   e

11

a   b   c   d   e

12

a   b   c   d   e

Total

TEST 7: **Analogies and Cubes**

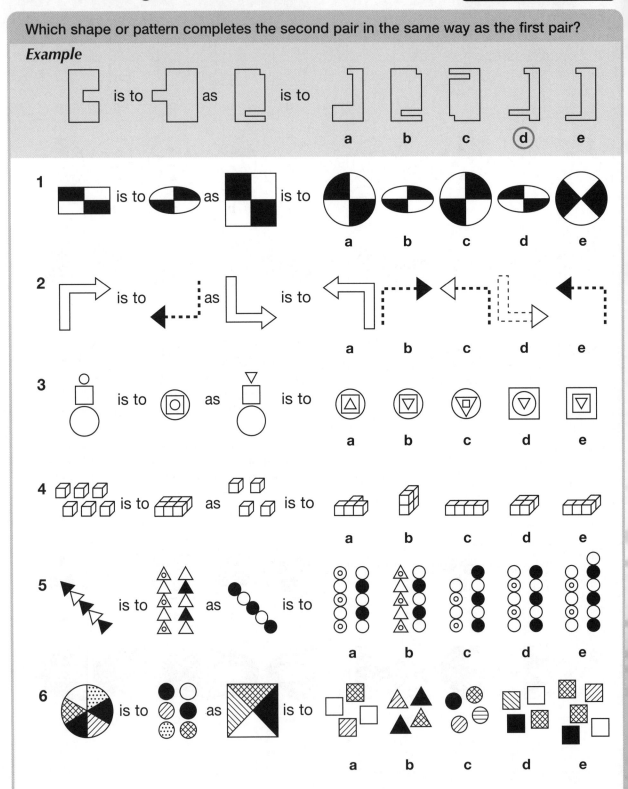

Which shape or pattern completes the second pair in the same way as the first pair?

Example

Which cube could not be made from the given net?

Example

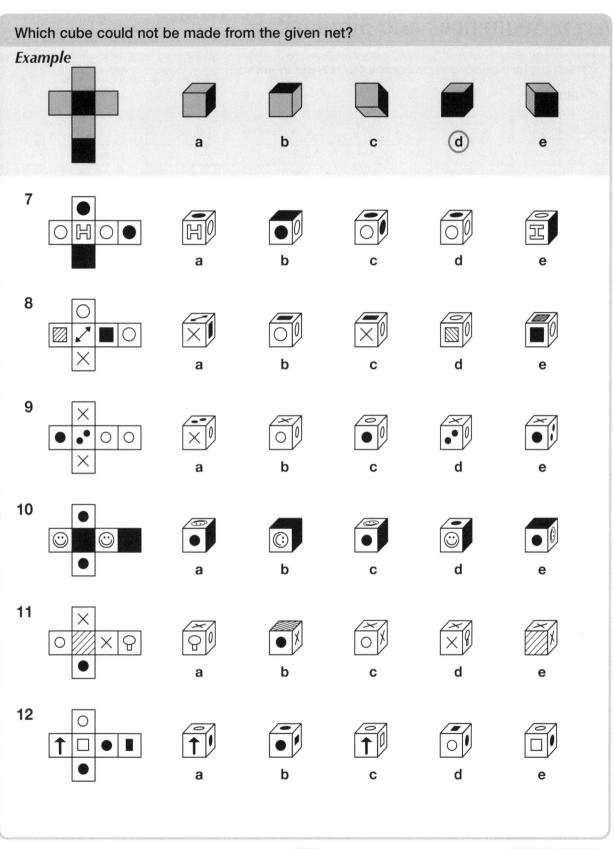

a   b   c   (d)   e

7

8

9

10

11

12

Total

Which pattern continues or completes the given series?

Example

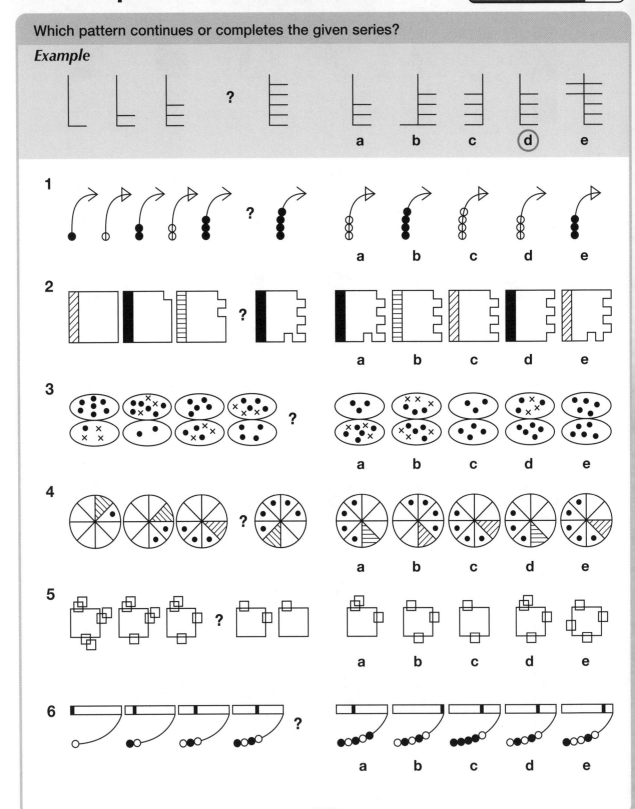

Which shape on the right goes best with the shapes on the left?

Example

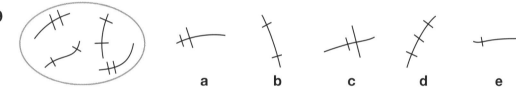

7

8

9

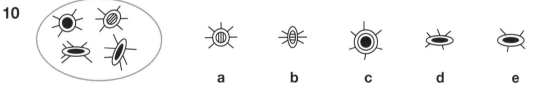

10

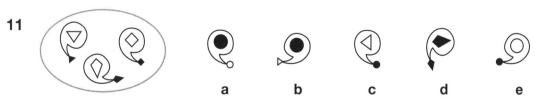

11

12

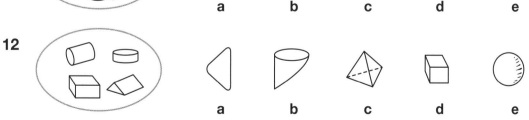

Which shape or pattern completes the second pair in the same way as the first pair?

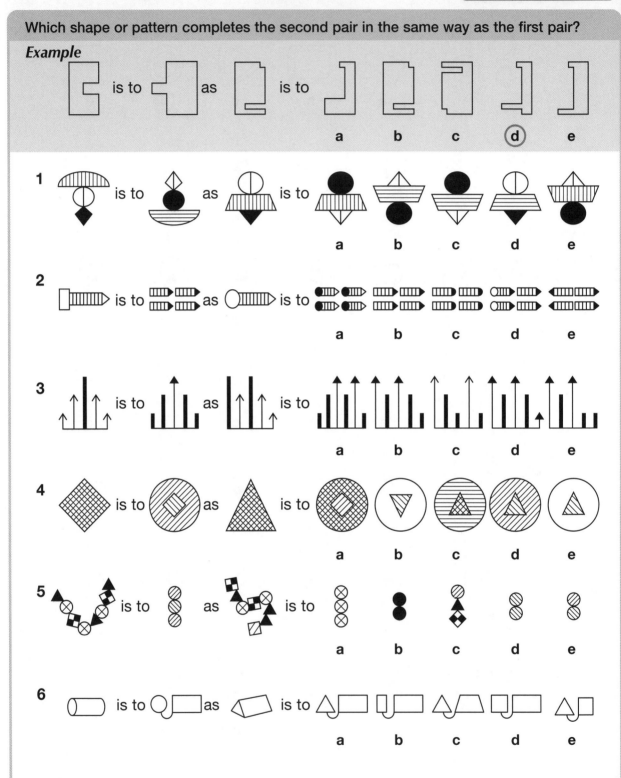

Example

a   b   c   d   e

1

a   b   c   d   e

2

a   b   c   d   e

3

a   b   c   d   e

4

a   b   c   d   e

5

a   b   c   d   e

6

a   b   c   d   e

18

Which shape on the right goes best with the shapes on the left?

Example

a   b   c   (d)   e

7

a   b   c   d   e

8

a   b   c   d   e

9

a   b   c   d   e

10

a   b   c   d   e

11

a   b   c   d   e

12

a   b   c   d   e

Total

Using the given patterns and codes, select the code that matches the last pattern.

Example

AX   AY   BZ   CY   BX   ?

AY   AX   CZ   BZ   BY
a   b   ⓒ   d   e

1

XL   XM   YN   ZN   YM   ?

ZL   XN   XL   ZM   YL
a   b   c   d   e

2

LD   MG   NF   OD   ME   ?

OG   LE   NE   MF   ND
a   b   c   d   e

3

AT   BV   BU   CU   CT   ?

AT   AV   CV   BT   CU
a   b   c   d   e

4

FA   DB   GA   DC   EB   ?

EA   DA   GC   GB   FB
a   b   c   d   e

5

LX   MY   NY   NZ   MX   ?

LY   MX   NX   LX   MZ
a   b   c   d   e

6

BF   DG   CF   AG   DH   ?

AF   DF   CH   AH   BH
a   b   c   d   e

Which cube could not be made from the given net?

Example

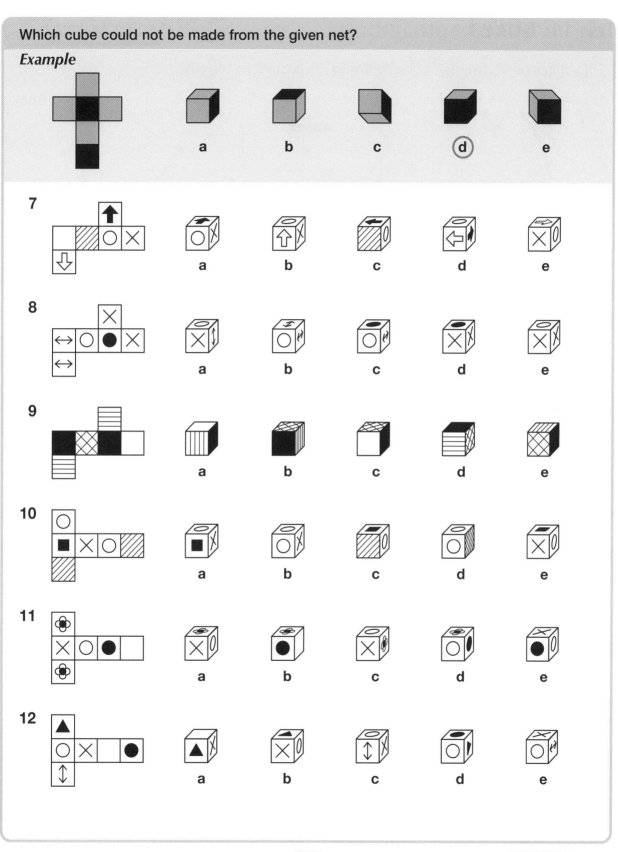

7

8

9

10

11

12

Total

Test time: 0 | | | | | 5 | | | | | 10 minutes

Which shape on the right goes best with the shapes on the left?

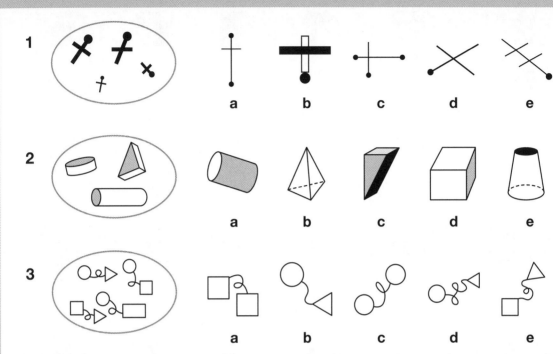

1

a   b   c   d   e

2

a   b   c   d   e

3

a   b   c   d   e

Which pattern continues or completes the given series?

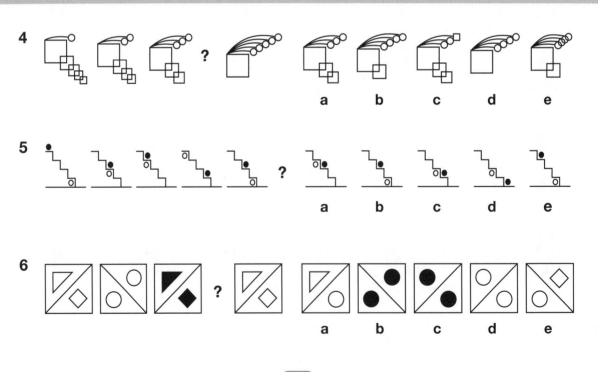

4

a   b   c   d   e

5

?

a   b   c   d   e

6

?

a   b   c   d   e

Which shape or pattern completes the second pair in the same way as the first pair?

7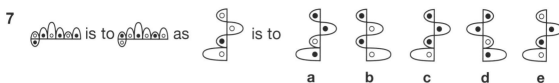

8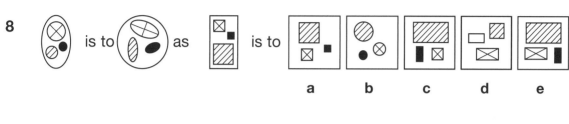

9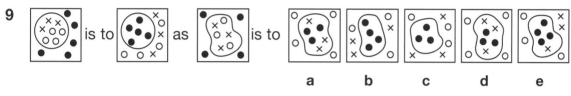

Using the given patterns and codes, select the code that matches the last pattern.

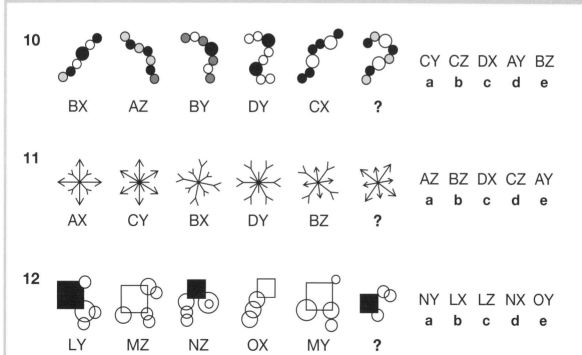

Test time: 0   5   10 minutes

Which pattern continues or completes the given series?

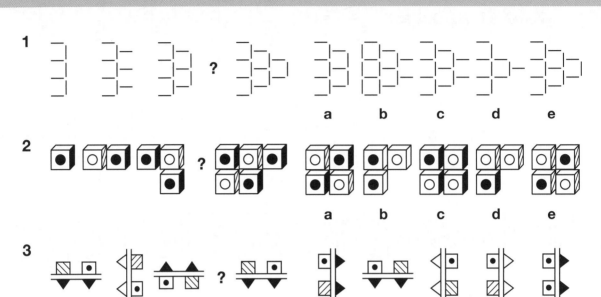

1

      a   **b**   **c**   **d**   **e**

2

      a   **b**   **c**   **d**   **e**

3

      a   **b**   **c**   **d**   **e**

Which cube could not be made from the given net?

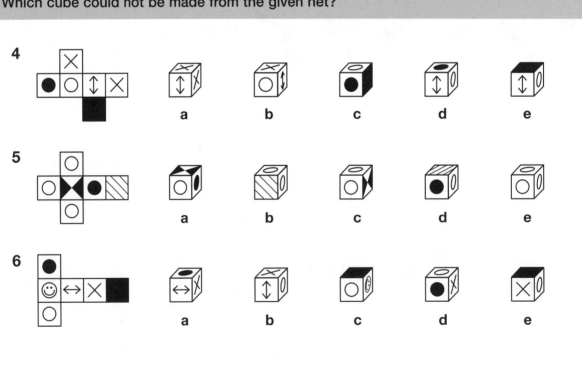

4

      a   **b**   **c**   **d**   **e**

5

      a   **b**   **c**   **d**   **e**

6

      a   **b**   **c**   **d**   **e**

1 **b** The first and alternate shapes in the sequence are inverted Vs.

2 **e** The column of white circles alternates with the black circles and decreases by two each time.

3 **e** The shape is rotated clockwise by 90° and after a full turn the shape decreases by two lines, one at each end of the pattern.

4 **c** The pattern of black spots alternates with the crosses and increases by two each time.

5 **d** The vertical line reduces in height along the sequence and the horizontal line increases in length, pointing to the right and left alternately.

6 **a** The shape increases with the alternate addition of a black spot and a white circle.

7 **d** The first letter represents the position of the small circle within the larger circle (A at the top, B on the right, C at the bottom). The second letter represents the shape at the bottom of the pattern (D a triangle, E a square, F a circle).

8 **a** The first letter represents the pattern of circles around the central circle (G is no circles, H is for one circle top right, J is for one circle top left). The second letter represents the shading style of the central circle (X is white, Y is diagonal lines, Z is black).

9 **c** The first letter represents the shading style of the rectangle (N is horizontal lines, P is black, M is diagonal lines, L is white). The second letter represents the pattern of the circles at the bottom of the shape (W is a large circle on small, Y is two small circles, V is two medium sized circles, X is a small circle on top of large).

10 **b** The first letter represents the number of plus signs in the shape (A is 1, B is 2, C is 3, D is 4). The second letter represents the outer shape (X is a circle, Y is a triangle, Z is a square).

11 **e** The first letter represents the angle of the line across the hexagon (A is diagonal bottom left to top right, B is diagonal top left to bottom right, C is horizontal). The second letter represents the shading pattern (S is half black half white, T is all shaded with cross-lines, U is half shaded with cross-lines).

12 **c** The first letter represents the shape at the top of the curve line (A is a black circle, B is a white circle, C is a 'sun', D a white 'sun'). The second letter represents the pattern of lines at the base (X is 2 lines, Y is 3 lines, Z is a zigzag).

1 **b** The first letter represents the direction of the arrow in the shape (A is up, B is to the right, C is down, D is to the left). The second letter represents the number of black spots (X is 4, Y is 3, Z is 1).

2 **c** The first letter represents the location of the triangle in relation to the circle (E across the circumference, D outside the circle, F inside the circle). The second letter represents the shading of the small circle (R is black, S is hatched lines, T is white).

3 **c** The first letter represents the number of lines in the zigzag excluding the edges of the square (A is 6, B is 7, C is 8). The second letter represents the shading and shape inside each square (H black square, G white square, J white circle, K black circle).

4 **c** The first letter represents the orientation of the L-shaped outline (L with right angle at top right, M with right angle at top left, N with right angle at bottom left). The second letter represents the white shape (X larger circle, Y triangle, Z smaller circle).

5 **a** The first letter represents the pattern within the small circles at each end of the triplet (A cross, B white circle, C black circle, D vertical line). The second letter represents the shape within the central circle of the triplet (X a small square, Y a small circle, Z a small triangle).

6 **d** The first letter represents the direction the arrow points (A up, B right, C down, D left). The second letter represents the shading of the circle (X white, Y half black and half white, Z black).

7 **e** The background black and white shape stays the same, the inner black and white shapes move to the outside of the larger shape.

8 **b** The arrows rotate 90° clockwise, and the arrowheads become inverted Vs and vice versa.

9 **d** The shape is divided into six parts 'cut' down the middle and twice across the shape, with the sections separated out.

10 **b** The shape is the same but smaller, with the top left white quarter shaded black, and the ×s become horizontal lines.

11 **e** The black shape becomes the shape for the main outline, and the outer dotted shape is reduced in size and goes inside the new main shape.

12 **e** The shape is rotated 180°, the white horizontal rectangle becomes black, and the black one becomes white.

Test 3 (pages 6–7)

1 **c** All the shapes in the set have a solid outside line, with a dotted inner line and a central curved shape.

2 **d** All the shapes in the set have four sides with the line style the same for all four sides.

3 **a** All of the shapes in the set have two identical small circles in the top two triangles and two ovals on the kite tail; each oval is either black or white.

4 **d** All of the shapes in the set have a thick black V-shape line, with a small black spot with four short lines.

5 **e** All of the shapes in the set have either a double plain line with a central dotted line and a black circle, or a double dotted line with a central plain line and a white circle.

6 **c** All of the curved line patterns in the set enclose four distinct spaces.

7 **e** The missing square is a reflection of the top left square in a diagonal mirror line from the bottom left of the grid to the top right.

8 **b** All the arrows point from the corner of each small square into the centre, rotating around the four corners in each row of the grid.

9 **a** The bottom row of the grid is the same as the top row, so the missing square will be the same as the top middle square.

10 **c** The outer triangles of the star have an alternating pattern.

11 **e** Diagonally opposite triangles within the central hexagon of the shape are reflections of the opposite triangle.

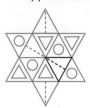

12 **d** The patterns in the triangles within the central hexagon each reflect the pattern diagonally opposite.

Test 4 (pages 8–9)

1 **a** The white oval goes up two then down one space along the sequence; the arrow alternates left then right, moving up one position in each pair.

2 **e** The C-shape of circles rotates 90° clockwise each time; there is always one large black circle in the top-right position. The colour of the three small circles alternates W–B–W and B–W–B each time.

3 **c** There are four columns in a repeating sequence so the next pattern will be the same as the third shape given in the sequence.

4 **b** The number of black circles follows the pattern 3–2–1–0–1– so the next pattern has two; the style of arrowheads at the ends of the vertical and horizontal lines alternate.

5 **c** All of the shapes have a linked triangle–square–triangle and the number of small white circles on the outside of these shapes increases by one along the sequence.

6 **d** The circle on top of the rectangle progresses along the top from left to right, the number of lines at the left end of the rectangle decreases by one as the number on the right increases by one.

7 **d** The first letter represents the shading style of the central circle (X is black, Y is striped, Z is white). The second letter represents the number of 'petals' and their shading (P is 5 white, R is 6 white, Q is 5 grey and S is 6 grey).

8 **a** The first letter represents the shading of the two small oval shapes (A both white,

B one black and one white, C both black). The second letter represents the numbers of lines (L is 2, M is 3, N is 4, O is 5).

9 **c** The first letter represents the shading style of the rectangle (A is white, B is diagonal lines, C is cross-hatched, D is grey). The second letter represents the number of shaded sections within the circle (X is 2, Y is 1).

10 **b** The first letter represents the style of the outer 'band' (E is narrow, F is wide, G is patterned). The second letter represents the position of the band around the cylinder (L at the bottom, M in the middle, N at the top).

11 **e** The first letter represents the pattern at the top of the shape (A is a single point, B is a wide shape, C is a double point). The second letter represents the style of the bottom lines (X is black pinheads, Y is white pinheads, Z is crosses).

12 **a** The first letter represents the number of white circles (C is 3, D is 4, E is 5). The second letter represents the number of black circles (W is 1, X is 2, Y is 3, Z is 4).

Test 5 (pages 10–11)

1 **c** The two ×-faces are opposite in the net so must be on opposite sides of the cube, they cannot be adjacent.

2 **e** One black face can be adjacent to the face with the black circle, but the second black face will be opposite the black circle so cannot be adjacent.

3 **b** The two faces with the double headed arrows are not adjacent in the net so cannot be adjacent in the cube.

4 **e** The face adjacent to the top of the T-face has a black circle, not the white circle.

5 **a** The face with the X is not adjacent to the white circle in the net so will be on opposite faces in the cube.

6 **d** The face with the cross and the face with the white square are not adjacent in the net so cannot be adjacent in the cube.

7 **d** All of the shapes in the set are composed of three elements.

8 **a** All of the shapes in the set have five sides.

9 **d** All of the shapes in the set have two loops with different shading styles in each loop.

10 **a** All of the shapes in the set have one straight line crossed by two straight lines.

11 **c** All of the rectangles in the set have a white border round an internal patterned smaller rectangle and they have an even fringe on one or both ends.

12 **c** All of the shapes in the set are symmetrical with a dotted line along the line of symmetry.

Test 6 (pages 12–13)

1 **c** The first letter represents the shading and relative position of the inner two circles (A is black inside white, B is black overlapping with white, C is white overlapping with white, D is white inside white). The second letter represents the outer shape of the pattern (X is a circle, Y is a triangle, Z is a square).

2 **b** The first letter represents the number of short lines (A is 2, B is 4, C is 6). The second letter represents the number of points on the stars (X is 4, Y is 5, Z is 6).

3 **b** The first letter represents the colour and shape at the top of the 'flagpole' (D a black oval, E a white oval, F a white diamond). The second letter represents the number of sections in the 'flag' (L is 2, M is 3, N is 4).

4 **a** The first letter represents the number of sections in the rectangles (S is 4, T is 3). The second letter represents the shading style of the circle (E is black, F is +, G is cross-hatched, H is ≡).

5 **d** The first letter represents the shapes (P for triangles, Q for quadrilaterals). The second letter represents the position of the dotted line shape in relation to the plain line shape (N is above, S is below, E to the right, W to the left).

6 **c** The first letter represents the pattern in the corner squares (A is white circle, B is black circle, C is black square, D is an ×). The second letter represents the pattern of the central square (E is white circle, F is black circle, G is black square, H is an ×).

7 **d** The inner white shapes become smaller and black, the number remains the same.

8 **d** The number of loops in the coil gives the number of zigzag elements along the line.

9 **e** Working from the bottom of the pattern the lowest shape goes inside the shape above, which is inside the one above it, etc.

10 **a** The pattern is rotated 180°, the white circles become black on long lines and the arrowheads are inverted on shortened lines.

11 **b** The elongated outer shape is 'squashed' so the oval becomes a circle; the inner shapes are also squashed to becomes squares and their shading changes to black).

12 **e** The shape is reflected with the shading styles changing from lines to black and vice versa.

Test 7 (pages 14–15)

1 **c** The corners of the shape become rounded, the white sections become black and vice versa.

2 **e** The arrow is rotated through 180°, the white outlines become a black dotted line with a black arrowhead.

3 **b** The top shape moves inside the middle shape, which moves inside the bottom shape.

4 **d** The individual cubes are placed together to form a regular cuboid on a horizontal plane.

5 **a** The line of shapes rotates 45° clockwise to a vertical position and becomes two lines. The black shapes become white with small white circles inside in the first column; the black shapes become white and vice versa in the second column.

6 **d** The shape stays the same but is reduced in size; the number of sections in the large shape gives the number of the smaller shapes; the shading style of each section of the large shape is replicated in one of the smaller shapes.

7 **d** The two faces with white circles are not adjacent and must be on opposite sides of the cube.

8 **e** The face with the grey lined square and the face with black square must be on opposite sides of the cube.

9 **c** The faces with the white circles are in a line with the face with the black circle so the black circle cannot be adjacent to both white circles when in a cube.

10 **b** The two black faces are on faces that will be on opposite sides of the cube so they cannot be adjacent.

11 **c** One of the faces with an × is opposite the face with the white circle so there cannot be two faces with × adjacent to the face with the white circle.

12 **a** One of the faces with a black spot will be adjacent to the bottom edge of the face with the black arrow, that is below the arrow not next to it; the other face with a black spot will be opposite the face with the arrow.

Test 8 (pages 16–17)

1 **a** Curved lines with black circles and an open arrowhead alternate with curved lines with white circles and closed white arrowheads and the number of circles increases every second shape.

2 **c** The number of small squares cut out of the sides of the rectangle increases by one each

time and the shading of the strip on the left of the rectangle follows the sequence: diagonal lines–black–horizontal lines–.

3 **a** The number of black spots in the upper oval decreases by one each time, the number of black spots in the lower oval increases by one each time and the three crosses alternate between the lower and upper oval.

4 **a** The shaded segment of the circle moves clockwise one place round the circle each time, the black spots increase by one each time, occupying the segments ahead of the progressing shaded segment.

5 **b** The number of small squares decreases by one each time, starting from the bottom side, then from the right side and then from the top.

6 **d** The black line across the rectangular bar moves progressively from left to right, the number of beads on the curved line increases by one each time, alternately adding a black or white bead to the bottom of the 'thread'.

7 **e** All of the shapes in the set are circles with black arrowheads projecting from them.

8 **a** All of the shapes in the set are made up of three overlapping circles of the same size, with the three sections where two circles overlap shaded.

9 **b** All of the shapes in the set are made up of single longer line crossed by two shorter lines of equal-length.

10 **b** All of the shapes in the set are ovals or circles with an inner shaded oval or circle; they all have six short lines projecting from them.

11 **e** All of the shapes in the set have the same shape on the outer pointed tip of the 'comma' as the shape in the middle; the outer shape is black and the inner one is white.

12 **d** All of the shapes in the set are regular three-dimensional solids with no dotted lines.

Test 9 (pages 18–19)

1 **b** The shape is rotated by 180°, the white element becomes black and the black becomes white with a line and the vertical shading of the third section becomes horizontal line shading.

2 **b** The one shape becomes a set of four identical shapes with the white shape at the right end becoming black at the end of each of the four, and there is no white shape at the left end of the four small shapes.

3 **b** The vertical arrows become vertical black bars and the vertical black bars become vertical arrows with black arrowheads.

4 d The first shape is reduced in size and placed in a circle, the cross hatch shading becomes diagonal top left to bottom right shading in the inner shape with shading from bottom left to top right in the surrounding circle.

5 e The number of circles with a cross gives the number of circles in the second part and alternate circles have diagonal line shading in opposite directions.

6 a The shape of the two faces shown of the 3D solid become two 2D shapes linked by a curved line.

7 a All of the shapes in the set are either squares with a triangle inside, or triangles with squares inside and the inner shape is always black.

8 e All of the shapes in the set are comprised of three elements.

9 c All of the shapes in the set are made up of an overlapping square and circle.

10 b All of the shapes in the set are arrows pointing to the top right (NE) and they all have just one arrowhead.

11 d All of the shapes in the set are made up of rectangles containing two smaller, equal rectangles.

12 c All of the shapes in the set are made up of ovals, within each oval and touching its inner edge, is a small white circle with a central black spot.

Test 10 (pages 20–21)

1 a The first letter represents the number of sections within the rectangle (X is 4, Y is 3, Z is 2). The second letter represents the pattern along the short sides of the rectangle (L is triangles, M is short lines, N is semi-circles).

2 c The first letter represents the style of the double lines (L is outer line plain with inner line dotted, M is outer dotted and inner plain, N is both plain, O is both dotted). The second letter represents the arrow style and orientation (D is white arrow pointing out, E is white arrow pointing in, F is black arrow pointing out, G is black arrow pointing in).

3 e The first letter represents the colour combination of the circles in the pattern (A is all black, B is all white, C is black and white). The second letter represents the total number of circles (T is 2, U is 3, V is 4).

4 b The first letter represents the number and position of the short lines (D is three vertical lines, E is two vertical and one horizontal, F is four vertical, G is four vertical and one horizontal). The second letter represents the style of the circle (A is white with thin line, B is

white with thick black line, C is black).

5 e The first letter represents the shading pattern of the first rectangle in each pattern (L is line shaded at the ends and black in the middle, M is white at the ends with line shaded in the middle, N is black at the ends with line shaded in the middle). The second letter represents the relative position of the second rectangle to the first one (X is level, Y is mid-way down, Z is the below).

6 d The first letter represents the shape surrounding the black spots and the number of spots in the shape (A is large circle with two spots, B is small circle with two spots, C is rectangle with two spots, D is a large circle with four spots). The second letter represents the outer shape (F is a circle, G is a square, H is an octagon).

7 d The two faces with arrows are projecting out on opposite sides of the net so they must be opposite in the cube.

8 e One of the faces with a cross will be adjacent to the face with a white circle, but the second face with a cross will be opposite the white circle face, so they cannot both be adjacent to the white circle face in the cube.

9 c The face with cross-hatched shading and the white face are not adjacent in the net so cannot be adjacent in the cube.

10 c When one of the faces with diagonal lines is at the front of the cube with the black square at the top, the face to the right must either be the cross or the other face with diagonal lines, the white circle cannot be adjacent on the right.

11 e The face with the cross is opposite the face with the black circle, so they cannot be adjacent in the cube.

12 b The face with the equilateral triangle has the base of the triangle parallel to the edge shared with the face with the white circle.

Test 11 (pages 22–23)

1 d All of the shapes in the set have two crossed lines, with both lines the same style and with a black spot at one end of one line.

2 d All of the shapes in the set are solid drawn with no dotted lines and with one flat plain face shaded grey.

3 e All of the shapes in the set are made up of two different shapes linked by a curvy line that has one loop in it.

4 b The overlapping squares at the bottom right of the shape reduce in number by one each time and the white circles on the curved lines from the top left corner increase by one each time.

5　**d** The black spot follows the pattern down two steps, up one, the white circle moves progressively up but 'underneath' the 'steps' on the inside and, after reaching the top, starts again at the bottom.

6　**b** The pattern of shapes is repeated in alternate squares, the shapes are white in the first two squares, then black in the next two, then white, etc.

7　**a** The line pattern remains the same, the white spots become black and vice versa.

8　**e** The outer elongated shape is made 'regular' so the oval becomes a circle and the rectangle becomes a square; the converse happens to the three inner shapes, which retain their original shading.

9　**b** The white circles and crosses in the inner shape move to the outer part of the square and the black circles in the outer part move into the inner shape, the numbers of each do not change.

10　**a** The first letter represents the number and colour of the large circles (A is none, B is one black, C is two white, D is two black). The second letter represents the total number of small circles (X is 5, Y is 6, Z is 7).

11　**a** The first letter represents the style and number of the longer arrows (A is 4 long lines with arrowheads, B is 4 long lines with Vs, C is 6 long lines with arrowheads, D is 6 long lines with Vs at the end of each); the second letter represents the style of the short lines (X is with Vs at the end, Y has plain lines, Z has arrowheads).

12　**d** The first letter represents the size and colour of the square (L is large black, M is large white, N is small black, O is small white). The second letter represents the number of circles in the shape (X is 3, Y is 4, Z is 5).

Test 12 (pages 24–25)

1　**c** The grid increases to the right by adding horizontal and vertical lines alternately, with a decreasing number of squares in each column.

2　**a** The number of cubes in the shape increases by one each time, with the colours of the circles and side faces changing in alternate patterns.

3　**d** The shape rotates 90° clockwise each time and the two triangles alternate from black to white.

4　**d** The face with the double ended arrow points to the face with the cross and at the other end points to the black face, it does not point to the face with the black circle.

5　**e** Two of the faces with the white circles are opposite each other so cannot be adjacent in the cube.

6　**d** The face with the black circle is opposite the face with the white circle so cannot be adjacent in the cube.

7　**c**

8　**d**

9　**e**

10　**a** The first letter represents the shape at the top of the pattern (L is circle with cross, K is square with single vertical line, M is circle with single vertical line, N is square with cross). The second letter represents the pattern of the base lines (A is three separate short lines, B is three lines joined at the left, C is three lines joined at the right).

11　**c** The first letter represents the direction of the arrow projecting from the circle (E is up, F is right, G is down, H is left). The second letter represents the style of the circle (X has a double line, Y has a single line).

12　**a** The first letter represents the number of triangles in the pattern (A is 3, B is 2 and C is 1). The second letter relates to the shading (P has black shading, Q has diagonal lines, R has no shading, S has grey shading).

Test 13 (pages 26–27)

1　**a** The line shape at the bottom of the pattern changes into a 3D container shape, the 'flower' pattern loses the line and is added to the side to the 'container'.

2　**c** The pattern in the bottom right square is repeated in all of the sections of the grid.

3　**d** The lines given form the sides of a regular 2D shape, retaining the lines or arrowheads at their ends, which project beyond the vertices of the shape.

4　**d** All of the shapes in the set have four 'loops' that project outwards.

5　**d** All of the shapes in the set have one

triangular tip projecting from the circle, and one band of pattern around the circle.

6 **e** All of the patterns in the set only have right-angled turns and only enclose one area.

7 **c**

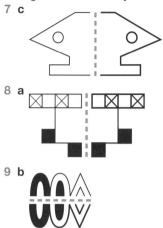

8 **a**

9 **b**

10 **d** The number of loops at the top of the curved line increases by one along the sequence and the number of small white circles decreases by one.

11 **e** The small black line at the right hand end of the top line moves to the left along the sequence, the black shaded rectangle in the bar moves one place to the right and the zigzag line at the bottom has an additional line added.

12 **a** The squares and circles alternate; in the squares, the small black circles in the lower left decrease by one and the number of L-shape lines in the top left increase by one along the sequence.

Test 14 (pages 28–29)

1 **e** The number of sides gives the number of horizontal lines and the white small shapes become black at the end of each line.

2 **c** The outer plain-lined shape only is reflected in a vertical line of reflection, the original plain outer line becomes dotted and the inner shape remains unchanged.

3 **a** The whole pattern is rotated 180° and the black shaded shape becomes white.

4 **d** All of the shapes in the set have two rounded projections and two rounded indentations.

5 **e** All of the shapes in the set are made up of five black dots with short lines between them.

6 **d** All of the patterns in the set comprise three elements.

7 **c** The first letter represents the number of small circles (A is 1, B is 2, C is none). The second letter represents the position of the

black circle in the column of circles (X is at the top, Y is in the middle, Z is at the bottom).

8 **b** The first letter represents the style of the rectangle (A tall and narrow, B square, C short and narrow, D short and wide). The second letter represents the shading of the circle (X is white, Y is diagonal lines, Z is black).

9 **a** The first letter represents the number of the arrow/pin shapes crossing the outline (E is 3, F is 4, G is 5). The second letter represents the shape and shading at the end of the short lines (U is white circle, V is black triangle, S is simple arrow, T is black circle).

10 **b** The face with the cross is opposite one of the faces with a white circle, and adjacent to the other, so it cannot be adjacent to both when in a cube.

11 **c** The half black/half white face is not adjacent to the face with the back circle in the net and must be on opposite faces in the cube, not adjacent.

12 **e** The two faces with the white circles are not adjacent in the net and so will be on opposite faces in the cube.

Test 15 (pages 30–31)

1 **d** The number of white circles decreases by one, the number of short vertical lines along the bottom increase by one and the position of the arrowhead and tail alternate.

2 **c** There is one less L-shape line in successive patterns along the sequence.

3 **e** The white circle moves along the pattern, alternating between being on top or below the rectangle, the black bar moves to the left two places, then back one to the right, then two to the left, etc.

4 **b** The first letter represents the orientation of the T element of the pattern (A has the 'junction' of the T at the top, B has it on the right, C has it on the bottom, D has it on the left). The second letter represents the style of the diagonal lines/arrows (X the arrows point inwards, Y the arrows point outwards, Z plain lines with no arrowhead).

5 **b** The first letter represents the style and number of the patterns on the corners of the squares (L two black spots with lines, M four black spots with lines, N two corners each with three lines, P four corners each with three lines). The second letter represents the central shape (S is a white circle, T is a cross-hatched circle, U is a black circle, V is a square).

6 **a** The first letter represents the small shapes around the large circle (X is white circles, Y is black circles, Z is black triangles). The second

letter represents the direction of the arrow (A is to the left, B is to the top, C is to the right, D is to the bottom).

7 e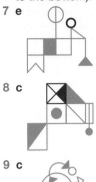

8 c

9 c

10 e All of the shapes in the set have five sides, with one black and one white circle inside them.

11 d All of the shapes in the set have a small white circle inside them and a small black circle on the outside, touching one of the corners

12 d All of the shapes in the set have a zigzag comprising five lines and one end has a black dot and the other end has a T-end.

Test 16 (pages 32–33)

1 c The face with the large X is opposite the white face in the net so cannot be adjacent in the cube.

2 e The face with the circle containing the cross is not adjacent to the face with the white circle in the net so they cannot be adjacent in the cube.

3 b When the face with the black square is at the top and the face with the candle is at the front, with the candle the right way up, then the face to the right must be the circle with a black spot.

4 e The shape at the top is repeated to make a column of three, with inverse shading in the top and bottom shape.

5 b The shape is rotated 90° clockwise and the white circle becomes black.

6 a The missing shape is made up of the top left quarter containing the pattern of shapes from the original bottom right quarter.

7 e All of the shapes in the set have two triangles joined by a short line, one triangle is all black and the other triangle is black with a white band along two of the three sides.

8 d All of the shapes in the set have one circle and two crosses all linked on a straight line.

9 b All of the shapes in the set are divided into quarters, with one quarter black, one lined and two white.

10 c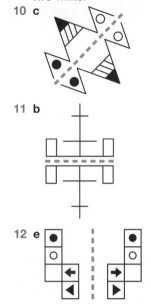

11 b

12 e

Test 17 (pages 34–35)

1 c The first letter represents the number of sections shaded black (A is 1, B is 2, C is 3, D is 6). The second letter represents the outer shapes (X is a circle/6-pointed star, Y is a hexagon/circle).

2 d The first letter represents where the horizontal line crosses the vertical line (A near the bottom, B near the top, C in the middle). The second letter represents the end shapes on the horizontal lines (S is black circle and black triangle, T is two black triangles, U is two white triangles, V is two black circles).

3 b The first letter represents the number of sides of the shape (L is 4, M is 5, N is 6). The second letter represents the number of black spots inside the shape (A is 3, B is 4, C is 5, D is 6).

4 a Each square is changed into three small circles with the middle circle projecting slightly to the right; each of the three groups of three circles replicates the shading patterns of the three squares.

5 e The straight lines change to a curved line in the same direction; the triangle at one end becomes a short line; the simple arrowhead becomes a solid black triangle.

6 b The outline shape becomes regular and the total number of circles gives the number of crosses inside the new shape.

7 e This is a repeating sequence of four patterns. The missing seventh shape will be the same as the third.

8 c The circle in the upper part of the oval alternates from white to black and the shape at the bottom follows a repeating pattern: black circle–black rectangle–striped circle– etc.

9 d The number of lines at the base decreases by one along the sequence, the angle between the diagonal line and the vertical increases each time and the black and white circles alternate.

10 d All of the shapes in the set have a semi-circle with a line from the curved edge joining the mid-point of one side of a square.

11 b All of the shapes in the set have a curved shape with diagonal shading, touching the edge of a black 2D shape with straight sides.

12 e All of the kite shapes in the set have a vertical line from top to bottom and one bow/flag on the attached 'string'.

Test 18 (pages 36–37)

1 b The first letter represents the number of black circles (A is 3, B is 2, C is 1, D is none). The second letter represents the number of triangles (X is 3, Y is 4, Z is 5).

2 c The first letter represents the direction that the arrow is pointing (F is up, G is to the right, H is down). The second letter represents the colour and position of the circles in relation to the U-shape (P is white and inside, Q is white and outside, R is black and inside, S is black and outside).

3 d The first letter represents the number of curly lines in the shape (A is 4, B is 3, C is 2). The second letter represents the number of points in the pattern where two lines cross (J is 3, K is 4, L is 5, M is 6).

4 e The top and the bottom shapes within the pattern are reflected is a vertical mirror line; the middle shape has its shading pattern reversed.

5 d The shape is rotated 180° and all of the dotted lines become solid lines.

6 e The curved arrows becomes straight arrows, the black triangular ends become simple arrowheads and the vertical shading lines become horizontal.

7 d The number of blocks in the rectangle decreases by one; the arrow alternates between being black and on the right, with a simple arrow on the left; and the circle alternates between being black and at the bottom with being white and at the top.

8 a One 'bead' or 'bar' on the top line moves from the left to the right each time, the white oval at the bottom also moves along from left to right.

9 a The shading of the oval alternates between small black oval within a white oval and solid black; the number of crossing points along the loopy curved line decreases by one each time.

10 d The face joining the bottom edge of the face with the 'T' has the circle on it not a square.

11 e The two faces each with two dots are not adjacent in the net and will be opposite each other in the cube, not adjacent.

12 e The face with the large cross and the face with the 'smiley face' are not adjacent in the net so cannot be adjacent in the cube.

Test 19 (pages 38–39)

1 c All of the patterns in the set have an 'H' shape with the top section enclosed and shaded; the base of the 'legs' of the H shapes have two small rectangles, one each side.

2 e All of the patterns in the set have five small lines within each 'bristle'.

3 a All of the patterns in the set have four white circles and two crosses.

4 c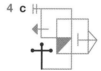

5 e

6 b

7 b The first letter represents the style of the white end of the shape (A is a white semi-circle with a forked line, B is a white semi-circle with an arrow, C is a white circle with an arrow, D is a white circle with a forked line). The second letter represents the style of the black end of the shape (X is a black triangle with a line, Y is a black semi-circle with two lines, Z is a black bar with two lines).

8 **a** The first letter represents the colour and size of the central square (E is large black, F is large white, G is small black, H is small white). The second letter represents the number of small squares with white circles in them (X is 1, Y is 2, Z is 3).

9 **e** The first letter represents the arrangement of the two thick black lines (A has one horizontal and one vertical, B both lines horizontal, C both lines vertical). The second letter represents the number of intersections in the pattern (X has 2, Y has 3 Z has 4).

10 **d**

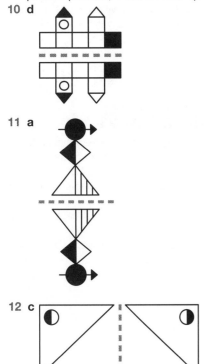

11 **a**

12 **c**

3 **a** The number of black dots at the top increases by one, the arrow alternates between pointing down and pointing up while progressing along the shape from left to right and the horizontal line alternates between solid and dotted.

4 **a** The 3D solid becomes a simple 2D face, the small shapes on the face switch from square to circle and vice versa and so does their black/white colour.

5 **b** The base of the 3D shape is drawn as a 2D shape and shaded black.

6 **c** The white squares become short black rectangles projecting on parallel lines, and the black spots that point down become white circles projecting to the right in line with the rectangles.

7 **e** The base edges of both faces with black equilateral triangles will be adjacent to the face with the cross and not the face with the white circle.

8 **c** The black face and the diagonally shaded face are not adjacent in the net, they will be opposite each other in the cube, not adjacent.

9 **a** The face with the arrow has the arrow pointing towards the face with the white circle not away from it.

10 **e** All of the shapes in the set have either three or five sides and only regular diagonal-line shading and black shading within them.

11 **c** All of the shapes in the set are cylinders, with a black circle in the middle of the circular face and a pattern of black and white bands around the cylinder.

12 **d** The patterns with the set all have a double headed straight arrow, a straight line with inverted arrowheads each end and a wavy line with a single black arrowhead.

Test 20 (pages 40–41)

1 **d** The angle between the two radii in the circle increases each time and the black circle alternates between the second and fourth position.

2 **b** The sequence of shapes from left to right along each row in turn is: triangle–circle–square–rectangle–etc.; the shapes in the bottom row of the grid are each divided into four sections.

Puzzle 1 (pages)

A

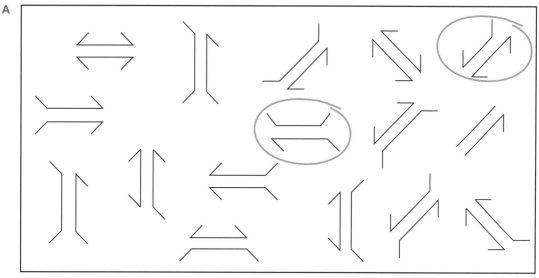

B

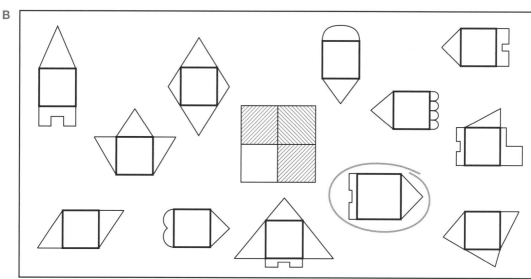

Puzzle 2 (pages)

A d
B c
C f
D g
E h
F c

Puzzle 3 (pages)

A c
B d
C b
D c
E d
F b

Puzzle 4 (pages)

A

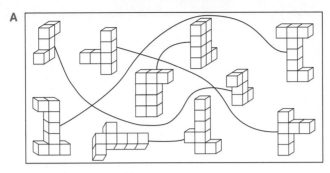

B

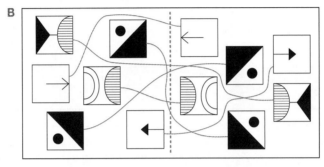

Puzzle 5 (pages)

A

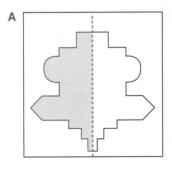

B

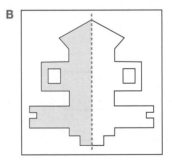

C

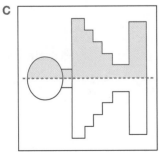

D

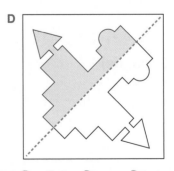

In which of the patterns is the given shape hidden?

Example

    a   b   c   (d)   e

7

    a   b   c   d   e

8

    a   b   c   d   e

9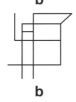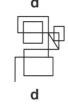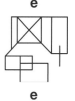

    a   b   c   d   e

Using the given patterns and codes, select the code that matches the last pattern.

10   

  LB   KA   MC   LA   NB   **?**

NC LC NA KC MB
a b c d e

11

  GY   EX   FY   GX   HX   **?**

FY EY FX GX HY
a b c d e

12

  AP   CP   BQ   BR   CS   **?**

CQ AQ BP AS CR
a b c d e

Total ▭

TEST 13: **Mixed**

Test time: 0 | | | | | 5 | | | | | 10 minutes

Which shape or pattern completes the second pair in the same way as the first pair?

1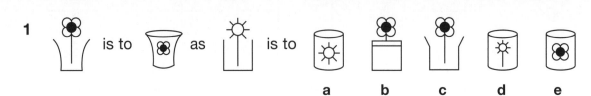

a	b	c	d	e

2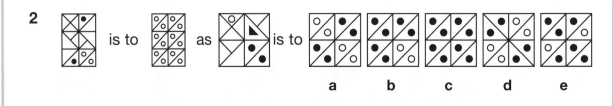

a	b	c	d	e

3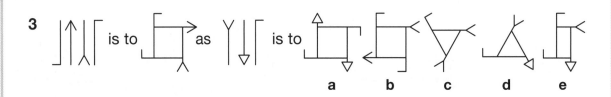

a	b	c	d	e

Which shape on the right goes best with the shapes on the left?

4
5
6

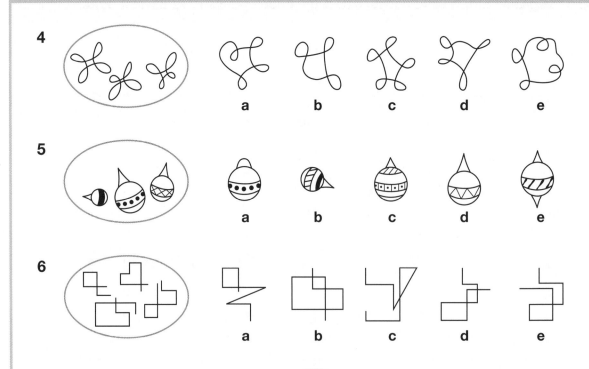

26

Which is the mirror image of the shape on the left?

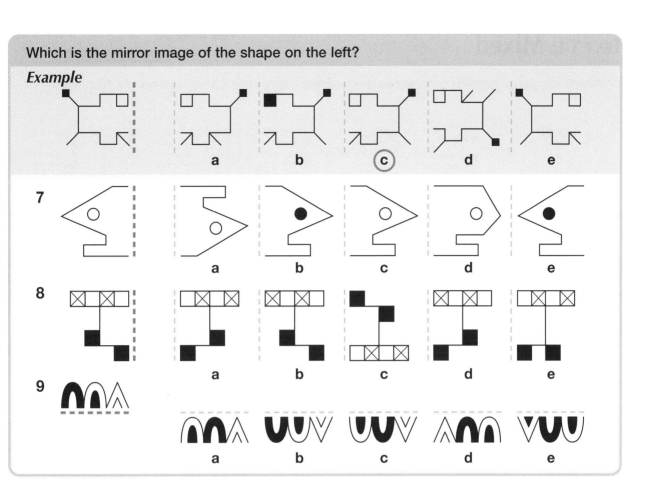

Example

7

8

9

Which pattern continues or completes the given series?

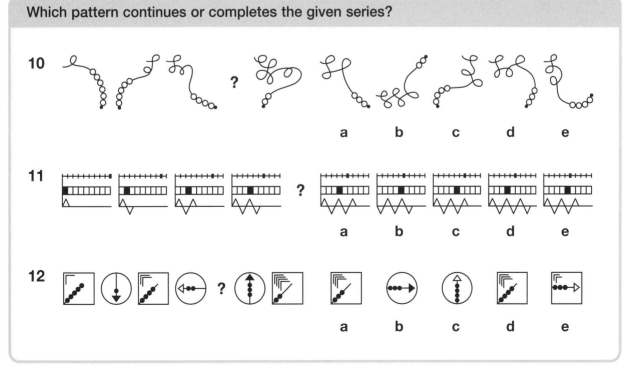

10

11

12

Total

Test time: 0

Which shape or pattern completes the second pair in the same way as the first pair?

1

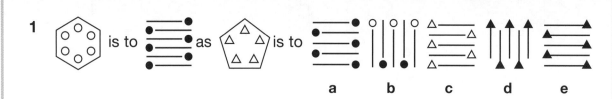

a   b   c   d   e

2

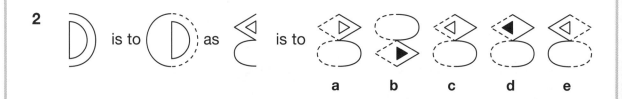

a   b   c   d   e

3

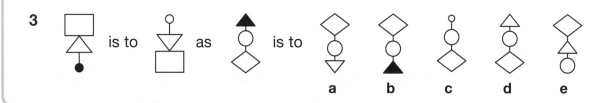

a   b   c   d   e

Which shape on the right goes best with the shapes on the left?

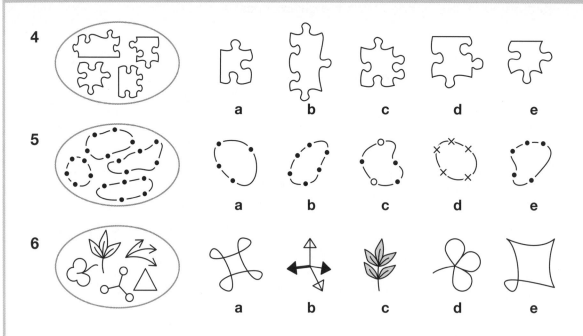

4

a   b   c   d   e

5

a   b   c   d   e

6

a   b   c   d   e

Using the given patterns and codes, select the code that matches the last pattern.

7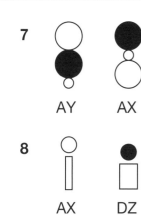

AY　　AX　　BX　　CZ　　BY　　?

BX AZ BZ CY CX
a　b　c　d　e

8

AX　　DZ　　DX　　BY　　CY　　?

CZ AZ BZ CX AY
a　b　c　d　e

9

GU　　FV　　GT　　ES　　FT　　?

EU FU EV ET GV
a　b　c　d　e

Which cube could not be made from the given net?

10 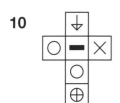　　　　　　

　　　　a　　　b　　　c　　　d　　　e

11 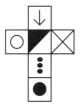　　　　　　

　　　　a　　　b　　　c　　　d　　　e

12 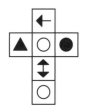　　　　　　

　　　　a　　　b　　　c　　　d　　　e

Total

TEST 15: Mixed

Test time: 0 ... 5 ... 10 minutes

Test time: 0 | | | | | 5 | | | | | 10 minutes

Which pattern continues or completes the given series?

1

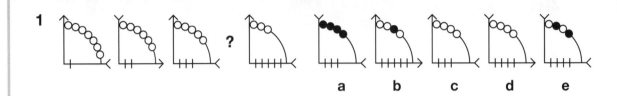

a   b   c   d   e

2

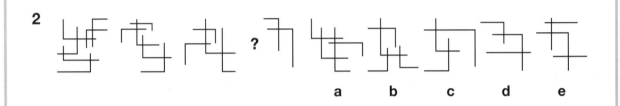

a   b   c   d   e

3

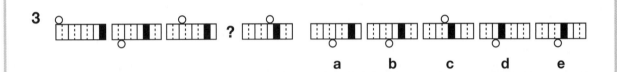

a   b   c   d   e

Using the given patterns and codes, select the code that matches the last pattern.

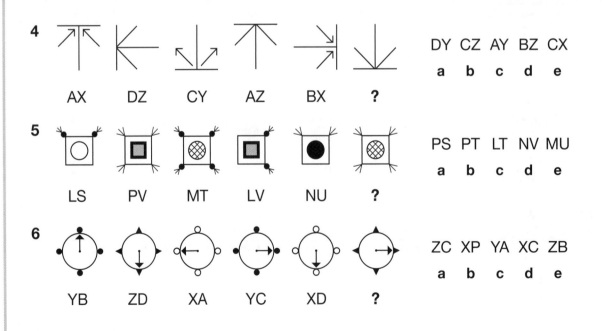

4

AX   DZ   CY   AZ   BX   ?

DY CZ AY BZ CX
a   b   c   d   e

5

LS   PV   MT   LV   NU   ?

PS PT LT NV MU
a   b   c   d   e

6

YB   ZD   XA   YC   XD   ?

ZC XP YA XC ZB
a   b   c   d   e

In which of the patterns is the given shape hidden?

7

  a   b   c   d   e

8

  a   b   c   d   e

9

  a   b   c   d   e

Which shape on the right goes best with the shapes on the left?

10

  a   b   c   d   e

11
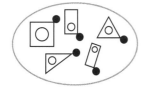

  a   b   c   d   e

12

  a   b   c   d   e

Total

TEST 16: Mixed

Which cube could not be made from the given net?

1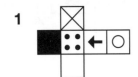

a   b   c   d   e

2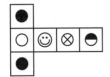

a   b   c   d   e

3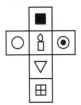

a   b   c   d   e

Which shape or pattern completes the second pair in the same way as the first pair?

4 is to as is to

a   b   c   d   e

5 is to 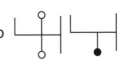 as is to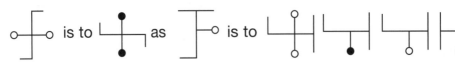

a   b   c   d   e

6 is to  as is to

a   b   c   d   e

Which shape on the right goes best with the shapes on the left?

7

                                               a   b   c   d   e

8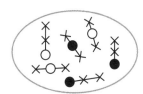

                                               a   b   c   d   e

9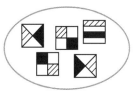

                                               a   b   c   d   e

Which is the mirror image of the shape on the left?

10

                                   a   b   c   d   e

11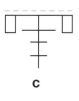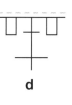

                                   a   b   c   d   e

12

                                   a   b   c   d   e

TEST 17: Mixed

Using the given patterns and codes, select the code that matches the last pattern.

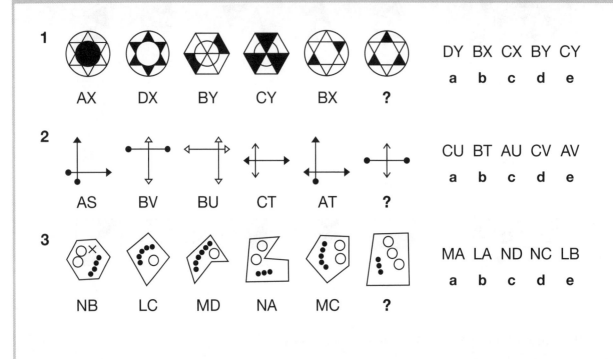

1   AX   DX   BY   CY   BX   ? | DY BX CX BY CY
                                      a b c d e

2   AS   BV   BU   CT   AT   ? | CU BT AU CV AV
                                      a b c d e

3   NB   LC   MD   NA   MC   ? | MA LA ND NC LB
                                      a b c d e

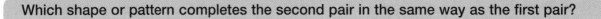

Which shape or pattern completes the second pair in the same way as the first pair?

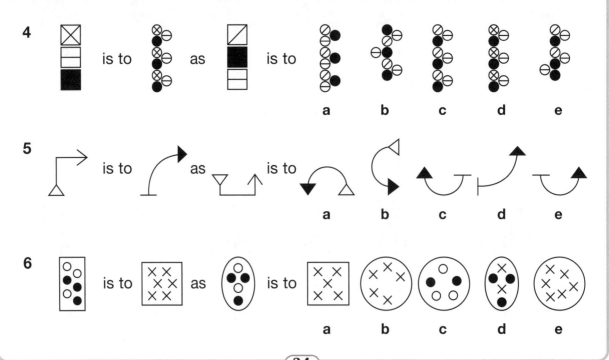

4   is to ... as ... is to   a b c d e

5   is to ... as ... is to   a b c d e

6   is to ... as ... is to   a b c d e

Which pattern continues or completes the given series?

7 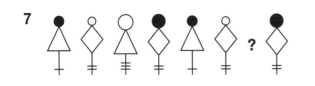 **?**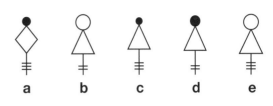

                  a   b   c   d   e

8  **?**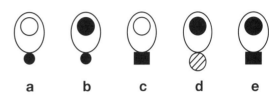

                  a   b   c   d   e

9 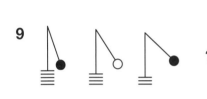 **?**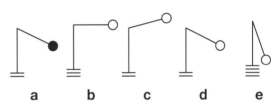

                  a   b   c   d   e

Which shape on the right goes best with the shapes on the left?

10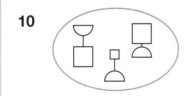

                  a   b   c   d   e

11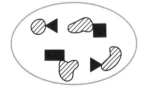

                  a   b   c   d   e

12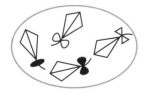

                  a   b   c   d   e

Total

TEST 18: Mixed

Test time: 0 ... 5 ... 10 minutes

Using the given patterns and codes, select the code that matches the last pattern.

1

AY   BZ   CZ   AX   DY   ?

CY CX BY AZ DX
a   b   c   d   e

2

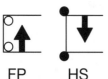

FP   HS   GR   HQ   GP   ?

GQ HP FS HR FR
a   b   c   d   e

3

AJ   BK   AM   BL   CK   ?

BM AK CJ BJ CL
a   b   c   d   e

Which shape or pattern completes the second pair in the same way as the first pair?

4

 is to as is to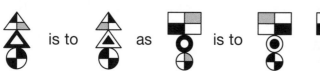

a   b   c   d   e

5

 is to as 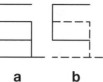 is to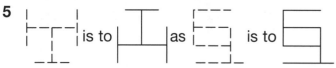

a   b   c   d   e

6

 is to as is to

a   b   c   d   e

36

Which pattern continues or completes the given series?

7

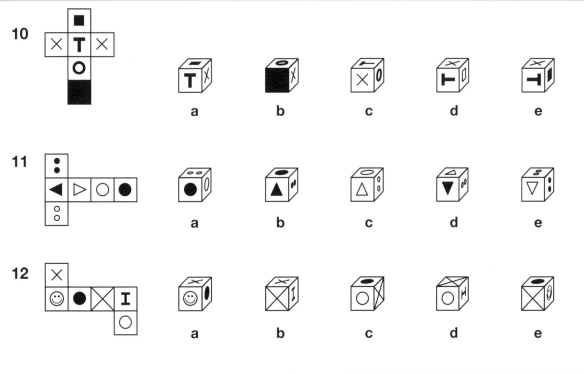

                              a   b   c   d   e

8

                              a   b   c   d   e

9

                              a   b   c   d   e

Which cube could not be made from the given net?

10
                              a   b   c   d   e

11
                              a   b   c   d   e

12
                              a   b   c   d   e

Total

TEST 19: Mixed

Which shape on the right goes best with the shapes on the left?

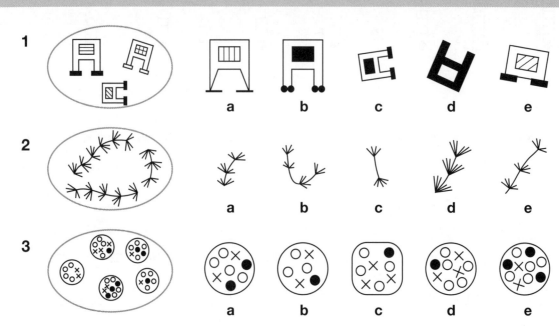

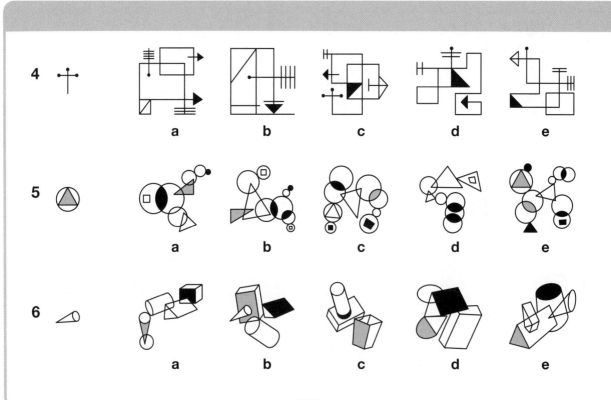

Using the given patterns and codes, select the code that matches the last pattern.

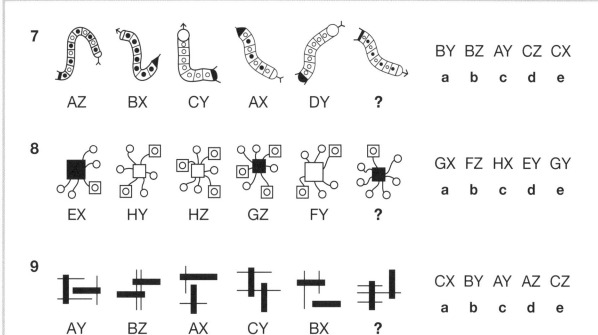

7

AZ   BX   CY   AX   DY   ?

BY	BZ	AY	CZ	CX
a	b	c	d	e

8

EX   HY   HZ   GZ   FY   ?

GX	FZ	HX	EY	GY
a	b	c	d	e

9

AY   BZ   AX   CY   BX   ?

CX	BY	AY	AZ	CZ
a	b	c	d	e

Which is the mirror image of the shape on the left?

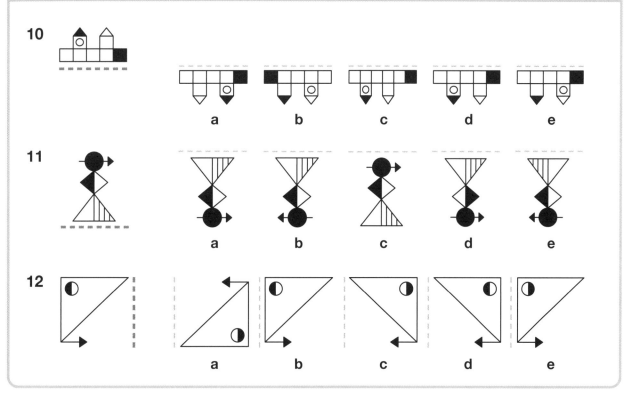

10

a   b   c   d   e

11

a   b   c   d   e

12

a   b   c   d   e

Total

TEST 20: **Mixed**

Which pattern continues or completes the given series or grid?

1  ?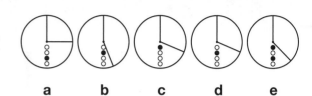

a b c d e

2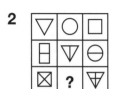

a b c d e

3 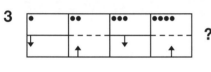 ?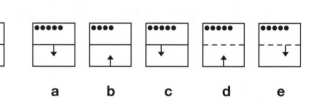

a b c d e

Which shape or pattern completes the second pair in the same way as the first pair?

4 is to  as  is to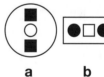

a b c d e

5  is to as  is to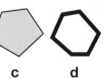

a b c d e

6 is to 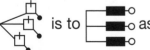 as is to

a b c d e

Which cube could not be made from the given net?

7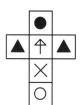

                                      a   b   c   d   e

8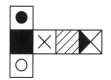

                                        a   b   c   d   e

9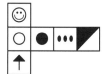

                                        a   b   c   d   e

Which shape on the right goes best with the shapes on the left?

10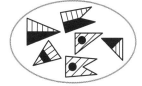

                                        a   b   c   d   e

11

                                        a   b   c   d   e

12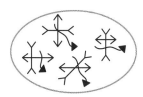

                                        a   b   c   d   e

Total

Puzzle ❶

Circle the two sets of parallel lines that are not equal in length.

A

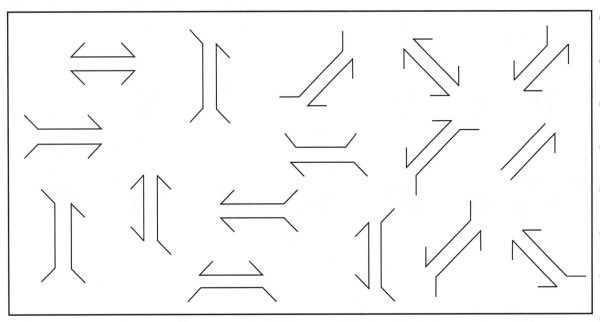

In which pattern is the bold square bigger than the white square in the middle.

B

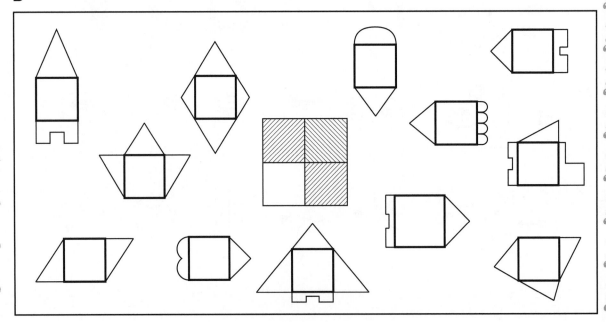

Puzzle ❷

In each box circle the pattern that is different from the rest.

A
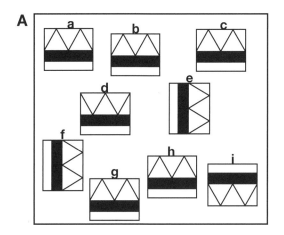

B
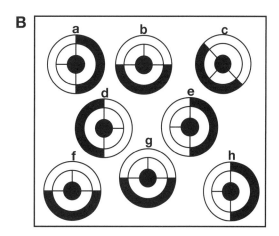

C

D
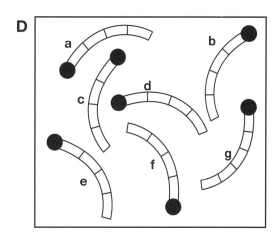

E
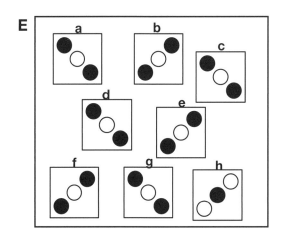

F
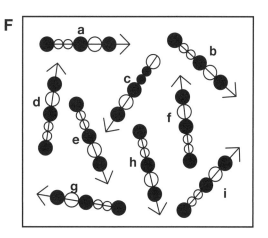

Puzzle ❸

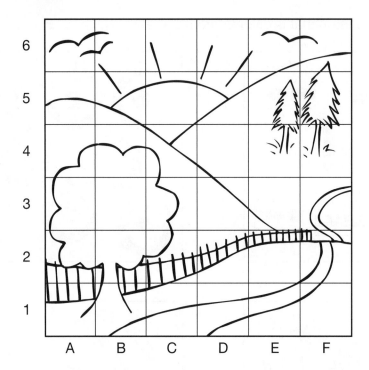

Which grid square is drawn below?

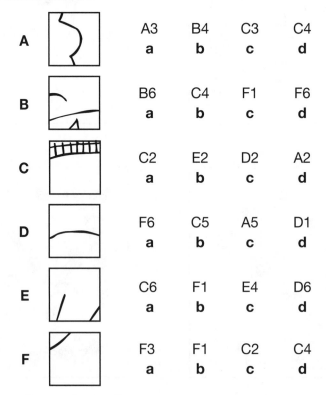

		A3	B4	C3	C4
A		a	b	c	d

		B6	C4	F1	F6
B		a	b	c	d

		C2	E2	D2	A2
C		a	b	c	d

		F6	C5	A5	D1
D		a	b	c	d

		C6	F1	E4	D6
E		a	b	c	d

		F3	F1	C2	C4
F		a	b	c	d

Puzzle ④

Identify and link the shapes that form a pair, in the same way as the pair already joined.

A

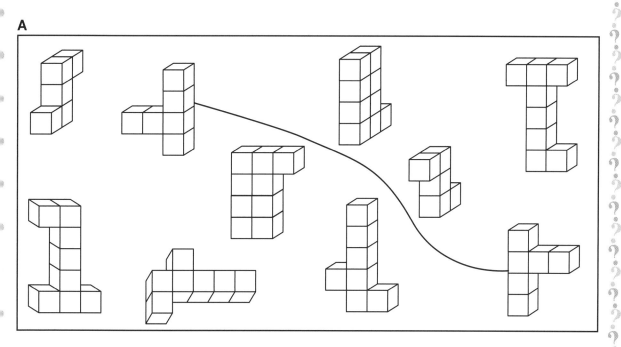

Join each shape on the left with its mirror image on the right.

B

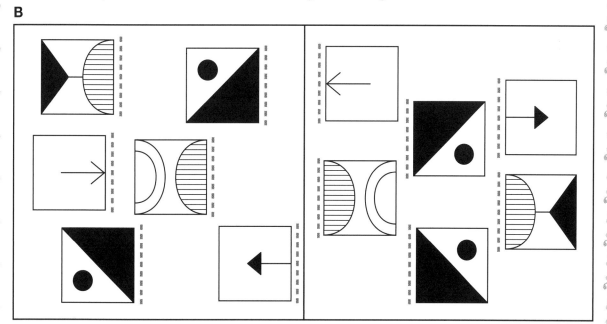

Puzzle 5

Complete these patterns by drawing their reflection in the dotted mirror line.
The first one has been started for you:

A

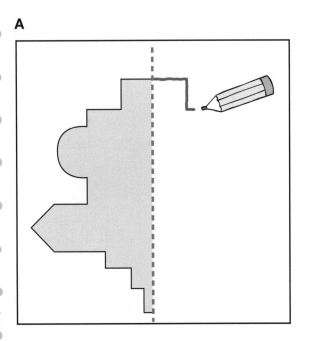

B

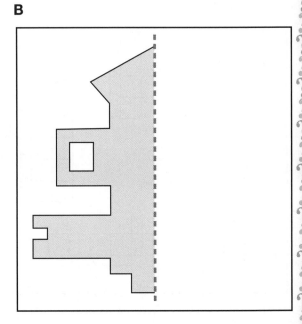

C

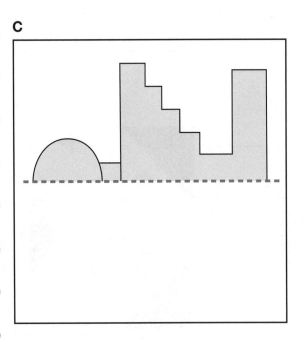

D

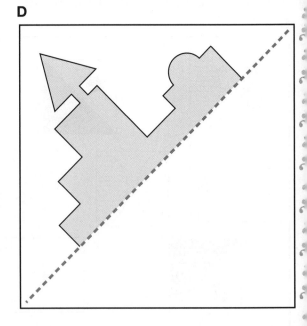

Progress Grid Non-verbal Reasoning 10 Minute Tests 10–11⁺ years

Total marks

Test